FIP handbook on practical design

FIP handbook on practical design

Examples of the design of concrete structures

Thomas Telford Limited, London

Published by Thomas Telford Ltd, Thomas Telford House, 1 Heron Q
London E14 9XF

First published 1990

British Library Cataloguing in Publication Data

FIP handbook on practical design.
1. Reinforced concrete structures. Design
I. Fédération Internationale de la Précontrainte
624.18341

ISBN: 0 7277 1570 4

Typeset in Great Britain by Santype International Limited, Salisbury, Wiltshire.
Printed in Great Britain by Staples Printers Rochester Limited, Love Lane, Rochester, Kent.

Preface

The *FIP recommendations: Practical design of reinforced and pre-stressed concrete structures (based on the CEB–FIP model code (MC78))*,[1] which were drawn up by the FIP Commission on Practical Design, were published in 1984. The main purpose of these recommendations was to provide practising engineers with a concise set of modern design rules, mainly based on the more comprehensive *CEB/FIP model code for concrete structures*[2] and the work of FIP commissions.

It has been widely felt that the feasibility and consequences of using these design rules should be demonstrated by means of comparisons with structures actually built, and that this would show practising engineers how the rules should be applied in different cases. This is the reason why the Commission undertook the calculations set out in the present document.

Eight structures which have recently been completed in various parts of the world are considered, and new design calculations are presented, carried out according to the design rules given in the recommendations.[1] In each case the calculations are preceded by some general remarks concerning the particular type of structure and the erection procedures applied. References are given to the relevant sections of the recommendations.

The calculations are presented at the stage of an approximate overall design: they could be used, for example, as a basis for tendering. More detailed examples can be found in the *CEB/FIP design manual on the application of the CEB/FIP model code for concrete structures*.[3]

The Comité Euro-International du Béton has been involved in the definition of the terms of reference of the present document. We acknowledge the excellent co-operation of the CEB, and especially their past President, Professor Tassios, and the present President, Dr Roy Rowe, who personally, after a final assessment of the eight examples, assured us that they are of particular interest to a wide audience and that they give a full picture of the design concept promoted by FIP and CEB.[1,2]

This handbook does not deal with the basic choice of the structural concept, which incidentally varies considerably from country to country, as may be seen from the examples treated. The structures chosen are not intended to be exceptional or outstanding, but rather ones which may be of interest for everyday design practice. The main aim is to treat particular design aspects of commonly used types and methods of construction by means of examples stemming from different countries.

The handbook is also intended to show what, and how, important design steps have to be taken according to actual design philosophies.

In spite of considerable efforts made at co-ordination, the styles of presentation of the examples differ somewhat, due to the different traditions regarding such calculations in the countries of the main authors.

As repetition has been avoided where possible, the individual examples should not be considered as complete calculations for the structures concerned. The exception to this is example A, which is an introduction to all checks needed for a simple case of a post-tensioned beam. Example B shows how the recommended rules may be applied in a rather complicated case of a pre-tensioned and post-tensioned bridge. Examples C to E give particular aspects of special kinds of erection: incremental launching, balanced cantilever construction and a cable-stayed bridge. Example F has been chosen in view of fatigue problems in a railway bridge, and examples G and H refer to partial prestressing of large industrial structures: a cement clinker silo subjected to high temperatures, and flat slabs with unbonded tendons.

The calculations performed show that the application of the FIP recommendations and their major basis—the CEB/FIP model code—is quite straightforward and simple and that the results are, in general, not very different from those obtained by observing the local codes on which the designs were initially based.

However, the clear distinction between *ultimate limit state* calculations and *serviceability limit state* calculations opens the way for better structural design as far as safety, serviceability and durability are concerned.

It is hoped that this handbook will be of help to those engaged in the design of structural concrete.

We acknowledge with gratitude assistance from outside the working group: Messrs C. Feyereisen (Lausanne) and W. Köhler (Vienna), both involved in the elaboration of example C, and Messrs C. de Cauwer (Lier), J.-J. Hitz (Yverdon), D. Horka (Trenčín), B. C. Jensen (Odense), M. Kalný (Prague), M. Koenigsberg (Jerusalem), P. Matt (Ittigen) and J. Stráský (Brno), who participated in the final checking of the examples. We owe special thanks to Mr W. F. G. Crozier, who did the final editing and a last control of certain numerical values.

Manfred Miehlbradt	Professor Dr René Walther
Co-ordinator of the handbook	President of FIP
Secretary of FIP Commission 3	Chairman of FIP Commission 3
on Practical Design	on Practical Design

References

1. *FIP recommendations: Practical design of reinforced and prestressed concrete structures (based on the CEB–FIP model code (MC78))*. Telford, London, 1984.
2. *CEB/FIP model code for concrete structures*. Comité Euro-International du Béton, Lausanne, 1978, MC78.
3. *CEB/FIP design manual on the application of the CEB/FIP model code for concrete structures*. Comité Euro-International du Béton, Lausanne, 1985, Bulletin d'Information 144.

Contents

Source publications

FIP recommendations: Practical design of reinforced and prestressed concrete structures (based on the CEB–FIP model code (MC78)). Telford, London, 1984.

CEB/FIP model code for concrete structures. Comité Euro-International du Béton, Lausanne, 1978, MC78.

Notation

A	area
A_c	area of plain concrete section
A_{c0}	loaded area
A_{c1}	geometric enlargement of loaded area
$A_{c\,ef}$	area of effective concrete embedment section
A_{ef}	area enclosed by mean perimeter of equivalent hollow section
A_p	area of prestressing tendons
A_s	area of tension reinforcement
A_{sf}	area of transverse reinforcement in flange
A_{sw}	area of legs of stirrups in each layer of shear reinforcement
A_{tot}	total area of concrete in compression zone
A_{tot}	total area of tension reinforcement
A_1	area of concrete in part of compression flange to one side of web
A_1	area of reinforcement in part of tension flange to one side of web
a	deformation
b	width of section
b	width of compression flange
b_f	width of flange
b_w	width of web
$b_{w\,nom}$	nominal web thickness
c	concrete cover
d	effective depth of tension reinforcement
d'	distance of reinforcement from the closest edge of the section
E_c	modulus of longitudinal deformation of concrete
E_{cm}	mean value of secant modulus of longitudinal deformation of concrete at 28 days
E_s	modulus of longitudinal deformation of steel
EI	flexural stiffness
e	eccentricity
F	force
F_c	concrete compressive force
F_{Rdu}	design value of local resisting force
F_s	steel tensile force
F_{Sd}	design value of acting force
F_{Sdu}	design value of local acting force
F_t	tensile force
f_{cd}	design value of concrete (compressive) strength (f_{ck}/γ_c)
f_{ck}	characteristic concrete (compressive) strength
f_{ctm}	mean value of concrete tensile strength
f_{cw3}	concrete compressive strength measured on cubes at age 3 days
f_{pd}	design strength of prestressing steel
f_{sk}	characteristic strength of (reinforcing or prestressing) steel
f_{tk}	characteristic tensile strength of prestressing steel
f_y	yield strength of reinforcing steel
f_{yd}	design strength of reinforcing steel
f_{yk}	characteristic strength of reinforcing steel
f_{yld}	design strength of longitudinal bars
f_{ywd}	design strength of stirrup reinforcement
$f_{0.1k}$	characteristic (0·1% proof) strength of (prestressing) steel
$f_{0.2}$	0·2% proof stress
G	permanent actions
G_1	permanent stabilizing actions
G_2	permanent non-stabilizing actions
g	permanent load
h	overall depth of section
h_{ef}	thickness of effective concrete embedment section
h_f	thickness of flange
h_t	depth of tension zone
I	moment of inertia
I_t	torsional moment of inertia
k	unintentional angular displacement per unit length

L	span
l	span
M	bending moment
$M_{act\,d}$	design value of acting moment
M_d	design moment
M_g	moment due to permanent load
M_o	decompression moment related to extreme tensile fibre in shear region under consideration
M_p	moment due to prestress
M_R	resistant moment
M_{Rd}	design value of resistant moment
M_r	cracking moment
$M_{res\,d}$	design value of resistant moment
M_{Sd}	design value of acting moment
M_{Sdu}	maximum design moment in shear region under consideration
M_u	ultimate moment
N	normal force
N_{Rd}	design value of resistant normal force
N_{Sd}	design value of acting normal force
P	prestressing force
P_i	initial value of prestressing force at origin
p	equivalent load due to prestress
Q	variable actions
Q_1	basic variable action
Q_2	other variable actions
q	variable load
R	support reaction
R_d	design value of resistant action effects
R_g	bearing reaction due to permanent actions
r	radius of curvature
S	action effect
S_d	design value of critical combination of action effects
S_e	action effect for one-mass system
s	spacing of bars
s_f	spacing of bars in transverse reinforcement in flange
s_w	spacing of shear reinforcement
T_{Rd}	upper limit of resistant torque
T_{Sd}	design value of acting torque
t	age of concrete
t_0	age of concrete at instant from which shrinkage or creep (commencement of loading) effect is being considered
u	perimeter of section in contact with atmosphere
V	shear force
V_{cd}	design value of resistant shear force provided by concrete in member with shear reinforcement
V_{Rd}	upper limit of resistant shear force, including effect of inclined tendons, in member with shear reinforcement
V_{Rd1}	design value of resistant shear force provided by concrete in member without shear reinforcement
V_{Rd2}	upper limit of resistant shear force provided by concrete in member with shear reinforcement
V_{Sd}	design value of acting shear force
V_{wd}	design value of resistant shear force provided by shear reinforcement
v_{Sd}	design shear force per unit length
W	modulus of inertia
W	resistance moment
w	crack width
w_k	characteristic crack width
x	distance along tendon measured from anchorage
x	neutral axis depth
y	distance from centre of gravity
y_o	distance of centroid from top
y_u	distance of centroid from bottom
z	lever arm

α	sum of angular displacements along tendon
α	modular ratio
α	inclination of shear reinforcement to longitudinal axis of beam
α_p	inclination of prestressing tendon to longitudinal axis of beam
γ	partial safety coefficient
γ_c	partial safety coefficient for concrete
γ_g	partial safety coefficient for permanent actions
γ_s	partial safety coefficient for steel
Δf_{sk}	characteristic fatigue strength of steel
ΔP	loss of prestressing force (immediate and time-dependent)
ΔR	additional support reaction
$\Delta \varepsilon_p$	tensile strain beyond ε_{pt} in bonded tendon at ultimate limit state
$\Delta \sigma_{p\infty}$	total loss of prestress after transfer due to time-dependent effects
$\Delta \sigma_{pi}$	loss of prestress due to friction between tendon and sheathing
$\Delta \sigma_{pr}$	loss of prestress due to relaxation
ε_c	concrete (compressive) strain
ε_{cs}	concrete shrinkage
ε_p	prestressing steel strain
ε_{pt}	tensile strain in tendon due to prestress after losses
ε_s	steel strain
ε_y	steel strain at yield or 0·2% proof stress
θ	inclination of concrete struts to longitudinal axis of member
λ	mechanical degree of prestress
μ	coefficient of friction between tendon and sheathing
ρ	tension reinforcement ratio (A_s/bd)
ρ_{id}	equivalent tension reinforcement ratio
ρ_r	tension reinforcement ratio
$\rho_{r\,min}$	minimum tension reinforcement ratio
ρ_w	shear reinforcement ratio
$\rho_{w\,min}$	minimum shear reinforcement ratio
σ	axial stress
σ_c	concrete (compressive) stress
σ_{cc}	limiting concrete compressive stress
σ_{cg}	stress in concrete at level of tendons due to permanent actions
σ_{cp0}	initial stress in concrete at level of tendons due to prestress alone
σ_{ct}	limiting concrete tensile stress
σ_p	stress in tendon
σ_{pg0}	initial stress in tendon due to prestress and permanent actions
σ_{pi}	initial stress in tendon during tensioning
σ_{p0}	initial stress in tendon after transfer due to prestress alone
σ_s	stress in reinforcing steel
τ	shear stress
τ_{Rd}	design value of resistant shear stress provided by concrete
ϕ	concrete creep coefficient
ϕ	nominal diameter of bar, wire, tendon or duct
ψ_0	combination coefficient for variable actions, other than a basic variable action, at ultimate limit state
ψ_1	combination coefficient for frequent value of variable actions at serviceability limit state
ψ_2	combination coefficient for quasi-permanent value of variable actions at serviceability limit state

Example A   Stockholm Globe Arena, Sweden: simply supported post-tensioned beams

Prestressing

Example prepared by B. Westerberg (Stockholm), with the assistance of J. Appleton (Lisbon), J.-P. Coppin (Brussels), W. Krüger (Wismar), M. Miehlbradt (Lausanne) and S. Rantanen (Espoo)

References to *FIP recommendations: Practical design of reinforced and prestressed concrete structures (based on the CEB–FIP model code (MC78))* are given in the right-hand margin

1. Introduction

A1.1. Prestressing techniques in building

A1.1.1. General

The choice between reinforced and prestressed concrete is governed by technical and economic factors. The typical technical advantage of prestressed concrete is the possibility of using large spans and/or slender structures, with cracking and deflections under control. Economically, a weight reduction can be favourable on bad soil, and also in seismic regions due to its lessening of the effects of seismic action.

The following prestressing techniques are used in housing construction

(a) pre-tensioning
(b) post-tensioning
    (i) bonded tendons
    (ii) unbonded tendons.

A1.1.2. Pre-tensioning

Pre-tensioning is used in precast elements, usually beams, slabs, and combinations such as double T beams. Pre-tensioning may also be advantageous in slender columns.

Tendons are usually wires or single strands. The force is normally transferred to the concrete by bond, without special end anchors.

Precast pre-tensioned elements probably represent the most common prestressing technique used in housing construction.

A1.1.3. Post-tensioning

Post-tensioning is used in connection with in situ casting. In housing construction this is mainly casting of beams and slabs, and sometimes casting of foundations. Soil and rock anchors are also examples of post-tensioning.

In post-tensioning, a major part of the dead load can be present as a counterweight when prestress is applied. In a precast, pre-tensioned element, only the self-weight of the element is there to balance the prestressing force. Therefore higher degrees of prestress are often possible in post-tensioning. The two methods can also be combined, by providing precast elements with ducts for post-tensioning on site, when additional dead load is present.

The use of post-tensioning varies from country to country. In many countries it is a frequent solution for slabs with spans greater than 6 m.

Bonded tendons

Bonded tendons represent the traditional post-tensioning technique. The prestressing force is transferred to the concrete by end anchors, but in the finished structure the tendons interact directly with the concrete by bond, in much the same way as for ordinary or pre-tensioned reinforcement. Cement grout injected into the ducts provides the bond, and also the necessary corrosion protection.

In many countries, post-tensioned bonded systems are quite common in housing construction (e.g. in beams and slabs). However, bonded tendons have some particular disadvantages in housing construction. One is the size of anchorage devices and tendons. To reduce tensioning and injection work, a few large tendons are preferable to many small ones. However, in a small cross-section, as in a slab, there is not enough space for heavy anchorages. Large tendons are less efficient than small ones with regard to the eccentricity. A special solution for slabs is to use flat ducts with several strands in one plane. A considerable amount of injection remains to be done, however.

Unbonded tendons

Unbonded tendons consist of single strands in plastic sheaths. The strands are greased for reduction of friction and protection against corrosion. Unbonded tendons have the following special advantages in housing construction.

(a) *Small dimensions.* A strand of 13 mm dia. has a sheath of 15–16 mm dia. and anchor plates about 60 mm × 110 mm.
(b) *No injection.* In a slab structure, often with hundreds of tendons, this means a substantial reduction of work.
(c) *Low friction losses.* Long tendons can be used, which reduces the amount of tensioning work.
(d) *Light stressing equipment.* A jack may weigh some 25 kg.

Disadvantages due to lack of bond must be considered. In the ultimate limit state of bending, the tensile stress is not much higher than the prestress, since the tendon is elongated over its entire length, instead of locally at cracks, as is the case for bonded tendons. The lack of bond also means that local failure of one or more tendons in one span leads to loss of prestressing force all the way between the end anchors, often involving several spans. Therefore the tendons must always be supplemented by enough ordinary reinforcement.

A1.2. Design principles

A1.2.1. General

The design principles for the finished structure are described in the FIP recommendations and (in more detail) by Comité Euro-International du Béton *et al.*[1]   *1.1*

Some complementary remarks concerning the construction phase are given here.

A1.2.2. Serviceability limit state

The serviceability of the finished structure is influenced by conditions in the construction phase. For example, if the concrete is loaded early, cracking may occur at stresses lower than those in the final stage. Early loading also increases creep deformations. These factors in combination can have a substantial influence on deformations in the final stage.

In a prestressed structure, the prestress may be chosen to balance the load in the finished structure. In this way cracking and creep deformations can be controlled. If only part of the dead load is present when the prestress is applied, special care must be devoted to the construction phase. The prestress may then be the dominating action, and the problem of cracking and deflections may be 'reversed'.

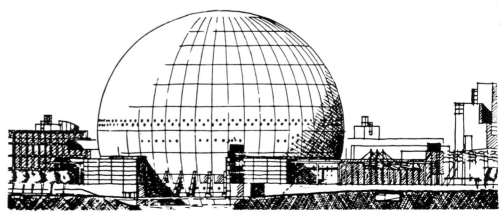

Fig. A1. The Globe

A1.2.3. Ultimate limit state

Safety in the construction phase may be critical, even if loads are lower than in the finished structure. First, the concrete strength when formwork is struck and/or tendons are tensioned is critical with regard to certain types of failure, such as shear and punching, anchorage failure, local crushing, and splitting behind tendon anchorages. Secondly, uneven load distributions in the construction phase may be critical for the curtailment of reinforcing bars in support regions, and possibly also for bending moments, since during the striking of formwork or concreting in upper stories some spans in a continuous slab are unloaded while others are loaded.

A1.3. Design example

This example deals with simply supported post-tensioned beams. The beams span 20·8 m and carry part of a concrete deck, the rest of which is an ordinary reinforced concrete slab supported on columns and walls.

The structure forms the floor of a training hall in the Globe Arena in Stockholm (Fig. A1). The hall will house an ice-skating rink and also be used for other purposes, in which case the floor may have a temporary floor laid on top.

Part of the basement under the concrete deck will be frequented by heavy lorries, requiring a free space about 20 m wide. Here the slab is supported on beams instead of columns. The required free height limits the total depth of structural concrete to 1·2 m in this area.

. Design data

A2.1. Structural system

The structural system is shown in Fig. A2.

The thickness of the slab varies from 150 mm to 250 mm. The bottom of the slab is horizontal, giving the top surface a slope of 1:100 for drainage of possible leakage water.

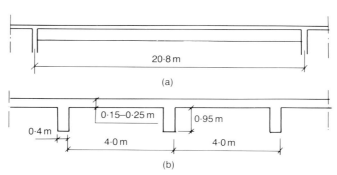

Fig. A2. Structural system

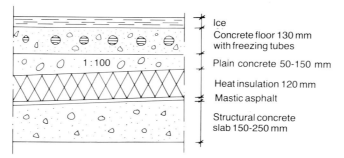

Fig. A3. Floor construction

On the slab there is water and heat insulation, mass concrete and a concrete floor with freezing tubes. The mass concrete provides the base for proper fixing of the tubes. The floor construction is shown in Fig. A3.

The permanent load will be high. To control long term deflections, a high degree of prestress is necessary. Therefore post-tensioned beams were chosen. The dead load of the slab is present when the prestress is applied, and the total load at this stage is about half of the final sustained load (including quasi-permanent variable load). The dead load of precast pre-tensioned beams would be only one fifth of the sustained load in this case, and the possible degree of pre-tensioning correspondingly lower.

A2.2. Loads
Permanent loads, from top to bottom

ice, up to 50 mm	0·5 kN/m^2
concrete floor slab, 130 mm	3·1 kN/m^2
mass concrete, 50–150 mm	1·2–3·6 kN/m^2
heat insulation, 120 mm	0·05 kN/m^2
mastic asphalt	0·45 kN/m^2
structural concrete	8·3–5·9 kN/m^2
installations	1·0 kN/m^2
total	14·6 kN/m^2

Permanent load per unit length of beam

$4 \times 14·6 = 58·4$ kN/m

Variable load (working load)   *Table*

characteristic value 4·0 kN/m^2

Variable load per unit length of beam

$4 \times 4·0 = 16·0$ kN/m

Combination coefficients   *Table*

frequent value: $\psi_1 = 0·5$

quasi-permanent value: $\psi_2 = 0·2$

The variable load is treated as a free action.

A2.3. Materials
Concrete grade: C35   *2.1.1*

Ordinary reinforcement   *2.2.1*

characteristic strength: $f_{yk} = 400$ N/mm^2 (beam)
characteristic strength: $f_{yk} = 600$ N/mm^2 (slab)

Prestressing strands   *2.3.1*

characteristic strength: $f_{0·1 k} = 1670$ N/mm^2
tensile strength: $f_{tk} = 1860$ N/mm^2
E-modulus: 195 kN/mm^2 *2.3.5*

Tendons

12 strands of 12·9 mm dia.
cross-section per strand: 100 mm^2
cross-section per tendon: 1200 mm^2
relaxation (final value): 5%

Serviceability ⁻ state

A3.1. Construction phase

A3.1.1. Tensioning of tendons

Calculations will be shown for the end and the midspan (Fig. A4). Tendon levels vary parabolically between these sections. Table A1 shows cross-sectional constants including the effect of duct holes and ordinary reinforcement (four bars of 25 mm dia.). (y is distance from bottom to centre of gravity.)

Load at this stage = dead load of concrete

$$g = 23 \cdot 6 \text{ kN/m at the ends}$$

$$g = 33 \cdot 2 \text{ kN/m at midspan}$$

$$M = 1 \cdot 62 \text{ MN m at midspan}$$

Maximum stresses in tendons at moment of tensioning   *3.2.1*

$$\sigma_{pi} \leqslant \begin{cases} 0 \cdot 80 f_{tk} = 0 \cdot 80 \times 1860 = \textbf{1490 N/mm}^2 \\ 0 \cdot 90 f_{0 \cdot 1k} = 0 \cdot 90 \times 1670 = 1500 \text{ N/mm}^2 \end{cases}$$

After transfer of prestress   *3.2.1*

$$\sigma_{po} \leqslant \begin{cases} 0 \cdot 75 f_{tk} = 0 \cdot 75 \times 1860 = \textbf{1395 N/mm}^2 \\ 0 \cdot 85 f_{0 \cdot 1k} = 0 \cdot 85 \times 1670 = 1420 \text{ N/mm}^2 \end{cases}$$

The tendons are tensioned from the same end in the order 3, 2, 1. For tendon 3 the highest permissible initial stress 1490 N/mm^2 is chosen, to compensate for the losses due to concrete deformation when stressing the remaining tendons. For the other tendons somewhat lower stresses are chosen.

Losses due to friction are calculated with $\mu = 0 \cdot 20$ and $k = 0 \cdot 01$ *3.3.2*
m^{-1}. The draw-in of anchorages is $\delta = 6$ mm according to the manufacturer.

Calculations are shown here for tendon 3.

Friction loss at midspan, $x = 10 \cdot 4$ m

$$\alpha = (0 \cdot 910 - 0 \cdot 298) \times 2/10 \cdot 4 = 0 \cdot 118$$

Table A1. Cross-section constants

	A: m^2	I: m^4	y: m
End	0·98	0·102	0·812
Midspan	1·38	0·132	0·913

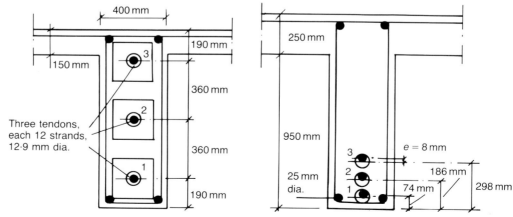

Fig. A4. Cross-sections at end and midspan

$$\Delta\sigma_{\text{pi}} = 1490 \times \{1 - \exp[-0.20 \times (0.118 + 0.01 \times 10.4)]\}$$
$$= 65 \text{ N/mm}^2$$

Draw-in of anchorage can be shown to give the loss

$$\Delta\sigma_{\text{pi}} = \sqrt{(\delta E_s \, d\sigma/dx)} = \sqrt{(6 \times 200 \times 65/10.4)} = 85 \text{ N/mm}^2$$

The prestress after these losses is

at stressing end, $\sigma_{\text{p0}} = 1490 - 2 \times 85 = 1320 \text{ N/mm}^2$

at midspan, $\sigma_{\text{p0}} = \text{min.} \begin{cases} 1320 + 65 = \textbf{1385 N/mm}^2 \\ 1490 - 65 = 1425 \text{ N/mm}^2 \end{cases}$

at passive end, $\sigma_{\text{p0}} \approx 1490 - 2 \times 65 = 1360 \text{ N/mm}^2$

After locking of the anchorages the stress varies along the tendon according to Fig. A5.

The results of calculations for the three tendons are shown in Table A2.

Table A2. Prestress in tendons (N/mm²)

Tendon	Stressing end	Midspan	Passive end
3	1320	1385	1360
2	1300	1350	1350
1	1274	1309	1330

Table A3. Stresses in tendons and concrete (N/mm²) after all immediate losses

	Stressing end	Midspan	Passive end
Tendon			
3	1309	1300	1349
2	1276	1295	1326
1	1274	1309	1330
Concrete			
Top	-1.3	0.5	-1.4
Level of tendons	-7.8	-13.2	-8.1
Bottom	-14.3	$\mathbf{-15.8}$	-14.9

Table A4. Stresses and deformations at midspan

Tendon(s) tensioned	Force: kN	Case	Concrete stress: N/mm²		Deformation: mm
			Bottom	Top	
3	1662	(a)*	-8.3	1.0	-15
		(b)†	2.9	-2.5	9
2(+3)	3233	(a)	-17.3	2.4	-31
		(b)	-5.9	-1.2	-8
1(+2+3)	4685	(a)	-27.0	4.0	-49
		(b)	-15.8	0.5	-25

* Formwork carries whole load.
† Structure carries whole load.

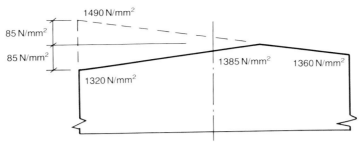

Fig. A5. Variation of prestress (tendon 3) due to friction and draw-in of anchorage

The loss in tendon j due to the concrete deformation when tendon i is tensioned is

$$\Delta\sigma_{\mathrm{p}ji} = \alpha P_i(1/A + e_i e_j/I)$$

where

$$\alpha = E_s/E_c = 195/32 \approx 6 \text{ (estimation)}$$

2.1.5

and P_i is force $\sigma_{\mathrm{p0}} A_{\mathrm{p}}$ in tendon i, e_i is eccentricity of tendon i, and e_j is eccentricity of tendon j.

Tensioning tendons 2 and 1 gives

at stressing end ($1{\cdot}300 \times 1{\cdot}2$ etc. $= \sigma_{\mathrm{p0}} A_{\mathrm{p}}$)

$$\Delta\sigma_{\mathrm{p}32} = 6 \times 1{\cdot}300 \times 1{\cdot}2 \times (1/0{\cdot}98 - 0{\cdot}262 \times 0{\cdot}098/0{\cdot}102) = 7 \text{ N/mm}^2$$

$$\Delta\sigma_{\mathrm{p}31} = 6 \times 1{\cdot}274 \times 1{\cdot}2 \times (1/0{\cdot}98 - 0{\cdot}622 \times 0{\cdot}098/0{\cdot}102) = 4 \text{ N/mm}^2$$

$$\Delta\sigma_{\mathrm{p}21} = 6 \times 1{\cdot}300 \times 1{\cdot}2 \times (1/0{\cdot}98 + 0{\cdot}622 \times 0{\cdot}262/0{\cdot}102) = 24 \text{ N/mm}^2$$

at midspan

$$\Delta\sigma_{\mathrm{p}32} = 6 \times 1{\cdot}385 \times 1{\cdot}2 \times (1/1{\cdot}38 + 0{\cdot}727 \times 0{\cdot}615/0{\cdot}132) = 41 \text{ N/mm}^2$$

$$\Delta\sigma_{\mathrm{p}31} = 6 \times 1{\cdot}309 \times 1{\cdot}2 \times (1/1{\cdot}38 + 0{\cdot}839 \times 0{\cdot}615/0{\cdot}132) = 44 \text{ N/mm}^2$$

$$\Delta\sigma_{\mathrm{p}21} = 6 \times 1{\cdot}309 \times 1{\cdot}2 \times (1/1{\cdot}38 + 0{\cdot}839 \times 0{\cdot}727/0{\cdot}132) = 55 \text{ N/mm}^2$$

Stresses in tendons and concrete after all immediate losses are shown in Table A3 (e.g. for tendon 3, stressing end, $1320 - 7 - 4 = 1309$).

Required concrete strength at the moment of stressing

$$f_{\mathrm{ck}} \geqslant 15{\cdot}8/0{\cdot}5 \approx 32 \text{ N/mm}^2$$

5.3.1

A3.1.2. Stresses and deformations in beams during tensioning

During tensioning, part of the load is carried by the formwork, due to its elasticity. The borderline cases are the following.

(*a*) The formwork carries the whole load.
(*b*) The structure carries the whole load (as assumed in previous calculations).

Stresses and deformations have been calculated for these two cases when the tendons are tensioned in the order 3, 2, 1 (Table A4).

Adding the prestressing force of one tendon, without increasing the load carried by the beam, will give an upward displacement relative to adjacent beams of 15–18 mm. This may damage the slab (see next section). To avoid this, each tendon must be tensioned in two steps, unless the formwork is fully or partially unloaded during tensioning.

A3.1.3. Deformation of slab during tensioning

When the tendons in one beam are tensioned, the slab will be deformed according to Fig. A6. If any torsional deformation of the beam is neglected, then

$$y = (1/r)a^2/6$$

$$1/r = 2\sigma/(E_c h)$$

which gives

$$\sigma = yE_c \times 3h/a^2$$

According to the preceding section, the full prestress of one tendon can give an upward displacement of 15–18 mm. With $E_c = 32$ kN/mm^2, the stress in the slab would be given by

$$\sigma \geqslant 15 \times 32 \times 3 \times 0{\cdot}25/3{\cdot}6^2 = 28 \text{ N/mm}^2$$

2.1.5

This means that cracking of the slab cannot be avoided, unless tension is applied in very small steps, or all beams are tensioned simultaneously, neither of which is practical. To avoid uncontrolled cracking, the reinforcement in the slab must permit a reasonable displacement without yielding. Fig. A7 shows the theoretical variation of the curvature in the slab. EI_1 is the bending stiffness in the uncracked state, EI_2 the stiffness in the cracked state and v is a reduction factor (MC78) taking account of the stiffening effect of concrete in tension

$$v = 1 - (M_r/M)^2$$

where M_r is the cracking moment.

The displacement possible without yielding of the reinforcement is calculated by integrating the curvature. The following values of yielding moment and corresponding displacement are obtained for a tensile strength of 3 N/mm^2 in the concrete and a yield strength of 600 N/mm^2 in the reinforcement. (A high yield strength is very favourable here.)

2.1.3

$\phi = 10$ mm, $s = 300$ mm   gives $M = 34$ kN m/m, $y \approx 5$ mm

$\phi = 10$ mm, $s = 250$ mm   gives $M = 41$ kN m/m, $y \approx 7$ mm

$\phi = 10$ mm, $s = 200$ mm   gives $M = 51$ kN m/m, $y \approx 11$ mm

The third case is chosen, since it allows tensioning without the restrictions being too severe. By measuring the displacement of each beam during tensioning and limiting it to 10 mm, tensioning can be performed without causing uncontrolled cracking in the slab.

A3.1.4. Time-dependent losses during construction

Before any additional load from the floor is applied, there will be prestress losses due to shrinkage, creep and relaxation. They are calculated separately because the load in this phase is only about half of that in the finished building. With this low load, the compressive stress in the concrete at the level of the tendons is high (cf. Table A4), giving considerable creep deformation. Shrinkage, creep and relaxation during the construction phase are estimated with regard to time, temperature and humidity (and stress levels in tendons).

A rough estimation of the loss is

$$\Delta\sigma_p \approx \varepsilon_{cs} E_s + \alpha\phi\sigma_c + \Delta\sigma_{pr}$$

where ε_{cs} is shrinkage, with an assumed value

$$\varepsilon_{cs} = 0{\cdot}04\%$$

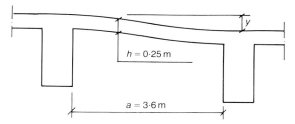

Fig. A6. Deformation of slab during tensioning

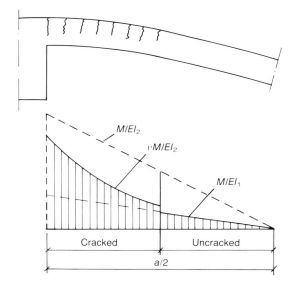

Fig. A7. Theoretical variation of curvature in slab

ϕ is creep coefficient, with an assumed value

$$\phi = 0.7$$

σ_c is compressive stress in concrete at level of tendons, 13·2 N/mm^2 at midspan and 7·8 N/mm^2 at end; $\Delta\sigma_{pr}$ is relaxation, with an assumed value

$$\Delta\sigma_{pr} = 1.5\% \sigma_{p0}$$

and σ_{p0} is average initial stress in tendons (values for tendon 2, representing the average tendon, are used).

At midspan

$$\Delta\sigma_p \approx 0.04 \times 195 + 6 \times 0.7 \times 13.2 + 0.015 \times 1295 = 83 \text{ N/mm}^2$$

At stressing end

$$\Delta\sigma_p \approx 0.04 \times 195 + 6 \times 0.7 \times 7.8 + 0.015 \times 1276 = 60 \text{ N/mm}^2$$

A3.1.5. Deformations during construction

The immediate deformations of the beams during tensioning are given in Table A4. With full prestress the beams will have a 'deflection' of -25 mm. During the construction phase, the negative deflection will increase by about 10 mm due to creep in the concrete; that is, the total upward deflection will be 35 mm or about 1/600 of the span. It will be neutralized later by the remaining permanent load (floor and installations) and some working load (see section A3.2.3).

A3.2. Finished structure
A3.2.1. Load values

The permanent load in the finished structure is

$q = 58.4$ kN/m

which gives at midspan

$M = 3.16$ MN m

Including the quasi-permanent value of the variable load

$q = 58.4 + 0.2 \times 16.0 = 61.6$ kN/m

$M = 3.33$ MN m

Including the frequent value of the variable load

$q = 58.4 + 0.5 \times 16.0 = 66.4$ kN/m

$M = 3.59$ MN m

A3.2.2. Time-dependent prestress losses

After injection of grout into the ducts, the prestressing steel can be included when the cross-sectional constants are calculated. The values obtained are shown in Table A5 (cf. Table A1).

The following values of total creep, shrinkage and relaxation are used

$\varepsilon_{cs} = 0.30\text{‰}$ *2.1.7*

$\phi = 2.5$

relaxation 5%   *2.3.3*

Subtracting the values used for the construction phase gives

$\varepsilon_{cs} = 0.26\text{‰}$

Table A5. Cross-section constants after injection of grout

	A: m^2	I: m^4	y: m
End	1·01	0·107	0·804
Midspan	1·41	0·148	0·897

Table A6. Stresses at midspan after losses

Load	Moment: MN m	Concrete stress: N/mm^2	
		Top	Bottom
Permanent only	3·16	−3·3	−2·4
Permanent + quasi-permanent	3·33	−3·6	−1·4
Permanent + quasi-permanent + frequent	3·59	−4·1	0·2

Table A7. Midspan deflections

Load	Midspan deflection: mm
Permanent, before time-dependent losses	−4
Including quasi-permanent, before time-dependent losses	−2
Including quasi-permanent, after time-dependent losses	2
Including frequent, after time-dependent losses	5

$\phi = 1.8$

relaxation 3.5%

When calculating losses, the mean stress and the mean eccentricity of the tendons are used, as follows.

At end

$\sigma_{p0} = \sigma_{pg0} = 1276 \text{ N/mm}^2$ (tendon 2)

$\sigma_{cp0} = -7.8 \text{ N/mm}^2$

$\sigma_{cg0} = 0$

$$\Delta\sigma_p = \frac{0.26 \times 195 + 0.035 \times (1276 - 0.3\,\Delta\sigma_p) + 6 \times 1.8 \times 7.8}{1 + 6 \times (7.8/1276) \times (1 + 1.8/2)}$$

$$= 166 \text{ N/mm}^2$$

3.3.3

At midspan, the stresses under the external moment of 1.62 MN m (cf. Table A3) are

$\sigma_{p0} = 1295$ (tendon 2)

$\sigma_{cp0} = -13.2 \text{ N/mm}^2$

and the stresses under permanent actions in the finished structure, with moment 3.16 MN m, are

$$\sigma_{cp0} + \sigma_{cg} = -13.2 + (3.16 - 1.62) \times 0.711/0.148$$

$$= -13.2 + 7.4$$

$$= -5.8 \text{ N/mm}^2$$

$$\sigma_{pg0} = 1295 + 6 \times 7.4 = 1339 \text{ N/mm}^2$$

$$\Delta\sigma_p = \frac{0.26 \times 195 + 0.035 \times (1339 - 0.3\,\Delta\sigma_p) + 6 \times 1.8 \times 5.8}{1 + 6 \times (13.2/1295) \times (1 + 1.8/2)}$$

$$= 142 \text{ N/mm}^2$$

A3.2.3. Stresses and deformations after losses

Total reduction of prestressing force

at midspan, $\Delta P = (83 + 142) \times 3600 \times 10^{-6} = 0.81 \text{ MN}$

at end, $\Delta P = (60 + 166) \times 3600 \times 10^{-6} = 0.81 \text{ MN}$

Stresses in concrete after losses

$$\sigma_{c\infty} = \sigma_{c0} + (M - M_0)y/I + \Delta P(1/A + ey/I)$$

where σ_{c0} is concrete stress after tensioning, M_0 is moment at tensioning (1.62 MN m), M is actual moment, y is distance from centre of gravity, and e is eccentricity of prestressing force.

The values obtained at midspan are shown in Table A6.

Similar calculations have been made for other cross-sections, although they are not presented here. The concrete stresses are low at midspan and there is no risk of cracking. It can also be seen that deformations will be small. The values obtained are shown in Table A7.

The total deflection of the finished structure is $5 + 4 = 9$ mm, which is only 1/2300 of the span.

Ultimate limit te

A4.1. Construction phase

A4.1.1. General

The ultimate limit state in the construction phase in this case concerns only the effects of prestressing forces in anchorage zones. After the anchorages are locked, the highest forces occur in the passive end of the beam. The forces corresponding to the stresses given in Table A2 are

$$P_1 = 1.60 \text{ MN}$$

$$P_2 = 1.62 \text{ MN}$$

$$P_3 = 1.63 \text{ MN}$$

With partial coefficient 1·35, the highest design value is

$$F_{Sd} = 1.35 \times 1.63 = 2.20 \text{ MN}$$

6.4.1

Design value of concrete compressive strength

$$f_{cd} = f_{ck}/\gamma_c = f_{ck}/1.5$$

4.1.3

Design value of reinforcement yield strength

$$f_{yd} = f_{yk}/\gamma_s = 400/1.15 = 348 \text{ N/mm}^2$$

4.1.3

A4.1.2. Local compressive stresses in the concrete
Loaded area with 250 mm square anchor plates

$$A_{c0} = 0.25^2 = 0.0625 \text{ m}^2$$

Design value of the resisting force

$$F_{Rdu} = f_{cd}\sqrt{(A_{c0} A_{c1})}$$

6.4.1

The anchorage spacing 0·36 m (Fig. A4) gives

$$A_{c1} = 0.36^2 = 0.130 \text{ m}^2$$

$$F_{Rdu} = f_{cd}\sqrt{(0.0625 \times 0.130)} = 0.090 f_{ck}/1.5$$

$$f_{ck} \geqslant 2.20 \times 1.5/0.09 = 37 \text{ N/mm}^2$$

With 0·25 m by 0·25 m anchor plates, the standard size for this type of tendon, tensioning cannot be done even at nominal concrete strength. For instance, when $f_{ck} = 30 \text{ N/mm}^2$, tensioning would require 0·3 m by 0·3 m anchor plates.

A4.1.3. Transverse tensile stresses in the concrete
Figure A8 shows the anchorages with the embedded spirals. The spirals are able to resist the local tensile stresses behind the anchorages, but where the spirals end the stresses are dispersed into the whole cross-section, causing tensile stresses for which reinforcement is needed.

6.4.2

The vertical tensile force at the upper anchorage will depend on the stress distribution in the concrete. Figure A9 shows the stress distribution at the end of the spirals, calculated with and without the slab.

Figure A10 shows the model used for calculating the vertical tensile force at the upper anchorage for the case shown in Fig. A9(a). The stress is multiplied by the width of the cross-section.

Moment equilibrium around A with the internal lever arm z assumed equal to the edge distance of the tendon at end of spiral (cf. Fig. A8) gives the tensile force

$$F_{sa} = 0.38 \text{ MN}$$

The same model applied to stress in Fig. A9(b) gives

$$F_{sb} = 0.18 \text{ MN}$$

With regard to dispersion of the prestressing force into the slab, the correct value is somewhere in between. Thus it is on the safe side to use

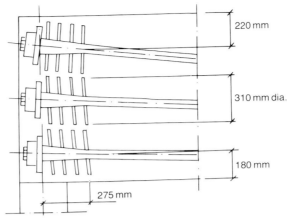

Fig. A8. Arrangement of anchorages with spirals

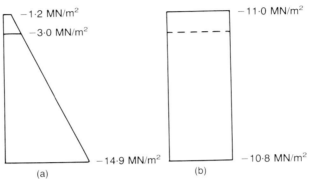

Fig. A9. Concrete stresses due to prestressing forces: (a) with 4 m width of slab included; (b) without slab

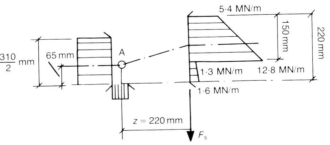

Fig. A10. Model for calculating vertical tensile force at upper anchorage

$$F_s = 0.38 \text{ MN} = 380\,000 \text{ N}$$

$$A_s = 380\,000/348 = 1090 \text{ mm}^2$$

which gives five stirrups of 12 mm dia.

This reinforcement is distributed in the region where the spirals end. One additional stirrup is placed just inside the anchor plates with regard to tensile stress occurring there.

Where the spirals end, some horizontal reinforcement is also placed. The tensile force can be calculated in the following way (0·3 m is the diameter of the spirals).

$$F = 0.3 \times F_{sd}(1 - a/b) = 0.3 \times 2.20 \times (1 - 0.3/0.4) = 0.17 \text{ MN} \qquad 6.4.1$$

$$A_s = 170\,000/348 = 490 \text{ mm}^2$$

which gives five bars of 12 mm dia. for each tendon.

A4.1.4. Transverse tensile stresses in the slab

Total force in flange according to Fig. A9(a)

$$F = 1.35 \times 0.5 \times (1.2 + 3.0) \times 0.15 \times (4 - 0.4) = 1.5 \text{ MN}$$

This gives longitudinal shear stresses between flange and web. The transverse reinforcement needed can be calculated in the same way as reinforcement for longitudinal shear due to external load (cf. section A4.2.4).

The shear force per unit length depends on the distance required for the flange to be fully interacting. With a dispersion 2:3 of the prestress (MC78) it can be estimated that

$$e \approx (h/2 + b_f) \times 3/2 = (1.1/2 + 1.8) \times 3/2 = 3.5 \text{ m}$$

$$v_{Sd} = 0.5 \, F/e = 0.5 \times 1.5/3.5 \approx 0.21 \text{ MN/m}$$

$$A_{sw}/s = 0.6 \, v_{Sd}/f_{yd} = 0.6 \times 210\,000/348 \approx 350 \text{ mm}^2/\text{m} \qquad \textit{4.4.3}$$

A4.2. Finished structure

A4.2.1. Design values

Design value of load

$$q_{Sd} = 1.35 \times 58.4 + 1.5 \times 16 = 103 \text{ kN/m}$$

Design value of concrete compressive strength

$$f_{cd} = f_{ck}/\gamma_c = 35/1.5 = 23 \text{ N/mm}^2 \qquad \textit{4.1.3}$$

Design value for prestressing tendons

$$f_{yd} = f_{0.1k}/\gamma_c = 1670/1.15 = 1452 \text{ N/mm}^2 \qquad \textit{4.1.3}$$

A4.2.2. Bending moment

$$M_{Sd} = ql^2/8 = 103 \times 20.8^2/8 = 5570 \text{ kN m}$$
$$= 5.57 \text{ MN m}$$

In this case the whole slab width can be included as flanges, i.e. $\qquad$ *7.1.4*

$$b = 4 \text{ m}$$

Average effective depth of tendons

$$d = 1.2 - 0.186 - 0.008 = 1.01 \text{ m}$$

Here 0·008 is the eccentricity of the cables in the duct holes (cf. Fig. A4).

Moment capacity of compression zone, assuming constant stress equal to $0.8f_{cd}$ within a depth $0.8x$ and no compression in the web $\qquad$ *4.3.2*

$$M_{R1} = b \times 0.8x \times 0.8f_{cd}(d - 0.4x)$$

Moment capacity of tendons

$$M_{R1} = A_p \sigma_s(d - 0.4x)$$

With the simplified stress–strain diagram for the steel, $\sigma_s = f_{yd} =$ $\qquad$ *2.3.4*
1452 N/mm². Combining the two equations gives

$$M_{R1} = 5.13 \text{ MN m}$$

The moment carried by 2×2 ordinary reinforcing bars of 25 mm dia., according to Fig. A4, is

$$M_{R2} = 2A_s f_{yd}(h - 2d')$$
$$= 982 \times 10^{-6} \times 348 \times (1.2 - 2 \times 0.053) = 0.37 \text{ MN m}$$

The total moment capacity is

$$M_{Rd} = M_{R1} + M_{R2} = 5 \cdot 13 + 0 \cdot 37 = 5 \cdot 50 \text{ MN m} < M_{Sd}$$

To obtain the necessary moment capacity at midspan, two more bars of 25 mm dia. have been added in the bottom of the cross-section (reserve in concrete compression zone).

A4.2.3. Shear force

The critical section is at a distance d from the support (d is effective depth with regard to ordinary reinforcement). 4.4.2(b)

$$d \approx 1 \cdot 05 \text{ m}$$

(cf. Fig. A4).

Acting shear force at the critical section

$$V_{Sd} = 103 \times (20 \cdot 8/2 - 1 \cdot 05) = 963 \text{ kN} = 0 \cdot 963 \text{ MN}$$

Minimum shear reinforcement

$$\rho_{w\,min} = 0 \cdot 15\%$$ 4.4.2(c)

$$A_{sw}/s = 0 \cdot 0015 b_w = 0 \cdot 0015 \times 0 \cdot 4 \times 10^6 = 600 \text{ mm}^2/\text{m}$$

Shear capacity of this reinforcement

$$V_{wd} = 0 \cdot 9d(A_{sw}/s)f_{ywd}$$ 4.4.2(b)
$$= 0 \cdot 9 \times 1 \cdot 05 \times 600 \times 348 \times 10^{-3} = 197 \text{ kN} = 0 \cdot 197 \text{ MN}$$

Concrete contribution to the shear capacity

$$V_{cd} = 2 \cdot 5\tau_{Rd} b_w d(1 + M_0/M_{Sdu})$$ 4.4.2(b)

where $\tau_{Rd} = 0 \cdot 38$ N/mm^2 for concrete C35, b_w is web thickness $= 0 \cdot 4$ m, $d = 1 \cdot 1 - 0 \cdot 05 = 1 \cdot 05$ m at beam end, M_{Sdu} is maximum design moment $= 5 \cdot 57$ MN m, and M_0 is decompression moment in the same section as M_{Sdu}.

$$M_0 = P(e + I/Ay)$$

Values at midspan

$$P = (1306 - 142 - 83) \times 3600 \times 10^{-6} = 3 \cdot 89 \text{ MN}$$

$$A = 1 \cdot 41 \text{ m}^2$$

$$I = 0 \cdot 148 \text{ m}^4$$

$$y = 0 \cdot 897 \text{ m}$$

$$e = 0 \cdot 703 \text{ m}$$

$$M_0 = 3 \cdot 89 \times [0 \cdot 703 + 0 \cdot 148/(1 \cdot 41 \times 0 \cdot 897)] = 3 \cdot 19 \text{ MN m}$$

The shear resistance of 'concrete' becomes

$$V_{cd} = 2 \cdot 5 \times 0 \cdot 38 \times 0 \cdot 4 \times 1 \cdot 05 \times (1 + 3 \cdot 19/5 \cdot 57) = 0 \cdot 627 \text{ MN}$$

The inclination of the prestressing force gives a contribution to the shear resistance of $P \sin \alpha \approx P \tan \alpha$. 4.4.2(b)

Prestressing force at beam end after losses

$$P = (1287 - 164 - 60) \times 3600 \times 10^{-6} = 3 \cdot 83 \text{ MN}$$

This value is used also for the critical section (where it is somewhat on the safe side).

$$\tan \alpha = (0 \cdot 550 - 0 \cdot 186) \times (1 - 1 \cdot 05/10 \cdot 4) \times 2/10 \cdot 4 = 0 \cdot 0629$$

$$P \tan \alpha = 3 \cdot 89 \times 0 \cdot 0629 = 0 \cdot 244 \text{ MN}$$

Total shear resistance

$$V_{Rd} = V_{wd} + V_{cd} + P \tan \alpha = 197 + 627 + 244 = 1068 \text{ kN}$$
$$= 1.068 \text{ MN}$$
$$> V_{Sd}$$

Minimum shear reinforcement is sufficient.

Spacing of stirrups of 12 mm dia.

$$s = 2 \times 113/0.600 \approx 375 \text{ mm}$$

However, maximum spacing is 300 mm, therefore values of   *4.4.2(c)*

dia. = 10 mm

$$s = 260 \text{ mm}$$

are chosen.

A4.2.4. Longitudinal shear (web–flange connection)
Longitudinal shear per unit length

$$v_{Sd} = (V_{Sd}/z)A_1/A_{tot}$$ *4.4.3*

where z is the internal lever arm, A_{tot} is total area of compression zone, and A_1 is part of A_{tot} on one side of web.

When the internal lever arm is reduced towards the ends, the value for the midspan can be used.

Assume

$$z \approx d - h_f/2 = 1.0 - 0.13 = 0.87 \text{ m}$$
$$A_1/A_{tot} = b_f/b = 1.8/4 = 0.45$$
$$v_{Sd} \approx V_{Sd} \times 0.45/0.87 \approx 0.52 V_{Sd}$$

Maximum value

$$V_{Sd} = 103 \times 10.4 = 1071 \text{ kN} = 1.071 \text{ MN}$$

which gives

$$v_{Sd} \approx 560 \text{ kN/m} = 0.560 \text{ MN/m}$$

Upper limit of longitudinal shear with regard to inclined compression

$$0.3 f_{cd} h_f = 0.3 \times 23 \times 0.15 \times 10^3 = 1035 \text{ kN/m} > 560$$

Transverse reinforcement in the flange

$$A_{sf}/s_f = 0.6 v_{Sd}/f_{yd} = 0.6 \times 560\,000/348 = 1000 \text{ mm}^2/\text{m}$$

Minimum value

$$0.0015 h_f = 0.0015 \times 150 \times 1000 = 225 \text{ mm}^2/\text{m}$$

This reinforcement should start at a distance from the support due   *Fig. 4.7*
to inclined cracking in web and flange. This distance is estimated as

$$d + b_f \approx 1.0 + 1.8 = 2.8 \text{ m}$$

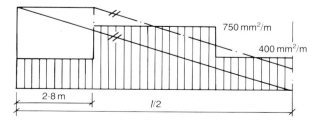

Fig. A11. Distribution of transverse reinforcement for longitudinal shear

Further away from the support, the reinforcement can be reduced with the shear force. Figure A11 shows the distribution of transverse reinforcement along the beam. Within 2·8 m of the support there is 350 mm²/m, according to section A4.1.4.

Drawings

Figures A12 and A13 show the beam reinforcement, slab reinforcement and beam end details. The drawings show only 'dimensioned'

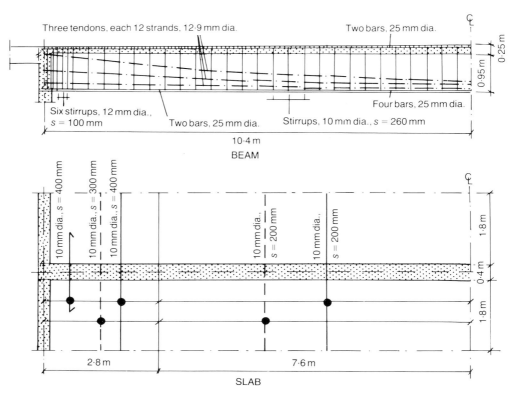

Fig. A12. Beam and slab reinforcement: in beam, ordinary reinforcement S400, prestressing tendons S1670/1860; in slab, reinforcement S600

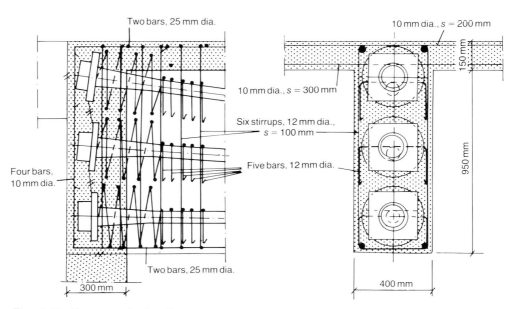

Fig. A13. Beam end: details

reinforcement. Some minimum longitudinal reinforcement in the web, e.g. two bars of 12 mm dia. in each side, could be recommended.

A6. Concluding remarks

The calculations according to the FIP recommendations have given essentially the same result as the original calculations according to the Swedish concrete code, which has been in use since 1980. The latter is largely based on MC78, although partial coefficients and detailing rules may differ.

In general, the calculations according to the FIP recommendations have given slightly more reinforcement. As an example, according to the Swedish code it is common practice to use the stress–strain curve of the prestressing steel. In this case, a simple linear interpolation between the yield and ultimate stresses would give an ultimate moment of 5·66 MN m instead of 5·13 MN m (section A4.2.2) according to the FIP recommendations, a difference of about 10%. Here it would mean that the two extra bars of 25 mm dia. (section A4.2.2) could be avoided. In addition to this, the partial coefficients in the Swedish code are generally somewhat lower.

Minimum requirements on reinforcement, such as stirrups in beams, are given only under certain circumstances in the Swedish code, e.g. with regard to fire. (For bridges, however, the minimum requirement is the same as in the FIP recommendations.) In this case, the original structure has only 56% of the total stirrup reinforcement obtained by these calculations.

The limitation of local compressive stresses according to the FIP recommendations is such that for the tendons in question the standard size of anchor plates cannot be used, not even if the concrete has reached its nominal strength at the time of tensioning. According to the original calculation, tensioning could be done at 75% nominal strength with standard anchor plates.

Reference

1. Comité Euro-International du Béton *et al. Common unified rules for different types of construction and materials*. CEB, Lausanne, 1978, Bulletin d'Information 124.

ample B   Bridge near Yverdon, Switzerland: single-span beam for multispan continuous road bridge

Pre-tensioning and post-tensioning

Example prepared by M. Miehlbradt (Lausanne), with the assistance of J.-P. Coppin (Brussels) and D. Lee (London)

References to *FIP recommendations: Practical design of reinforced and prestressed concrete structures (based on the CEB–FIP model code (MC78))* are given in the right-hand margin

Introduction

The motorway bridge near to Yverdon in Switzerland has a total length of more than 3 km, an overall width of 23–30 m and a height above ground of 6–10 m. There are good ground conditions below about 10 m.

The bridge is the result of a competition with fixed-price tender, where the main criteria were economy, aesthetics and construction method (in that order). For aesthetic reasons, the superstructure was required to consist of one deck (over the full width), supported in the transverse direction by a limited number of piers; and the longitudinal spans were required to be 30 m or longer. The total construction time was limited to 39 months; this included the construction of a special span of 72 m with a skew of 35°, to cross a future canal between the Rhine and the Rhône.

The winning design was for a bridge with a total cost (including foundations) of 450 SFr/m², a typical span of 32 m, and a mean superstructure thickness of 305 mm. The bridge was built during 1979–82.

The deck contains 604 precast beams (cast in a factory about 70 km from the site), and is completed by a cast-in-situ slab and pier diaphragms. The total depth is 1·82 m, in both the main spans and the special span of 72 m, but the special span has a bottom slab added, and the full section there has been cast in situ.

The prestress in the precast beams consists of strands and a first tendon stressed and grouted in the factory. As shown in Fig. B1, these beams were on temporary supports, allowing the slab form-work to move from the preceding span to the new position. The formwork for the diaphragm was then erected, the tendons were coupled to those of the preceding span, the reinforcement was placed and the concrete was poured. All this was done from Monday to Friday; the next Monday the continuity tendons were stressed and the following span could start.

The economy of the bridge is due in part to the rather sophisticated combination of precast elements and in situ concrete. All 604 beams were cast in the same mould; and the slab formwork was completely mechanized and could travel on the bottom flanges of the beams. The consoles and barriers were added in later stages. In addition, the whole structure is quite light, and thus the foundation costs were relatively low.

The following redesign according to the FIP recommendations concerns only the normal part of the superstructure with respect to bending in the longitudinal direction: it does not contain shear design, or checks in the transverse direction (slab), or calculations for the diaphragm, piers and pier foundations. The redesign is based on the original layout of the prestress and results in about the same reinforcement. Section B5 shows how simply the theory of plasticity can be applied, even in such a complicated case, and section B6.3.1 shows that the results of a detailed calculation of creep effects could be estimated quite simply. As in the original project, there are no problems concerning working stresses, deformations, crack control or minimum reinforcement, largely in agreement with results from the main calculations.

Design
mation

B2.1. Structural summary
See Figs B1–B6.

System (Fig. B1)
Normal span $l = 32 \cdot 15$ m of continuous bridge of 5×640 m approx. (total length = 3·155 km).

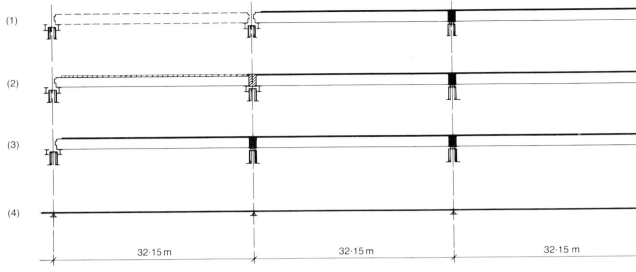

Fig. B1. Construction scheme

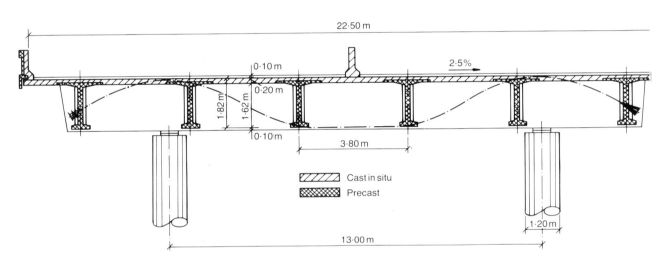

Fig. B2. Cross-section of bridge and diaphragm on piers

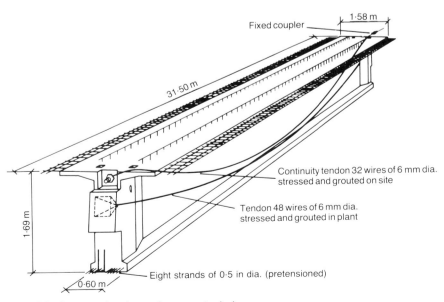

Fig. B3. Isometric view of precast girder

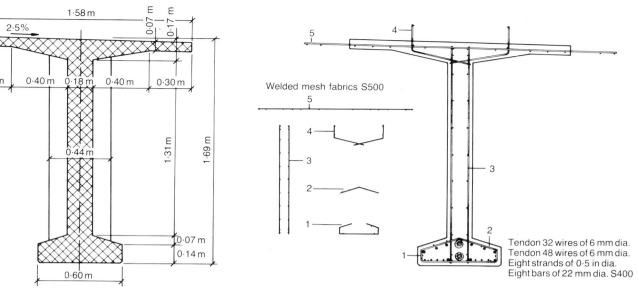

Fig. B4. *Cross-section of precast girder (including basic reinforcement)*

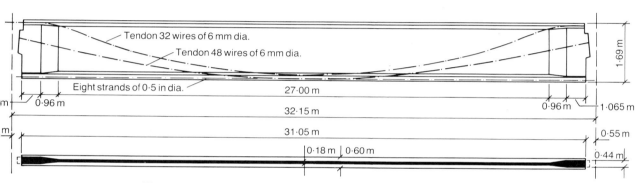

Fig. B5. *Precast girder (including tendon layout)*

Cross-section (Fig. B2)

Six precast T beams (spacing 3·80 m) connected by 0·20 m thick in situ slab (scaffolding supported by precast beams).

Prestressing (Fig. B3)

(*a*) Straight strands at bottom (precast girder).
(*b*) First parabolic tendon (precast girder).
(*c*) Second parabolic tendon for continuity.

(*a*) and (*b*) applied on single-span beams 3 days after casting; (*c*) applied 2 weeks after concreting of slab (acts on complete section) and connected by coupler to previously constructed span.

Diaphragm on piers (Figs B1 and B2)

Cast together with deck slab, post-tensioned.

B2.2. Materials

Concrete

Precast beam	C40
In situ slab	C30

Reinforcing steel

Reinforcing steel	S400
Welded wire fabric	S500

Prestressing steel
Strands 0·5 in   S1580/1820 ($f_{0 \cdot 1k}/f_{tk}$)
Eight strands: $A_p = 744$ mm^2
Wires 6 mm dia.   S1540/1770
Fatigue strength

$\Delta f_{sk} = 150$ N/mm^2 (strands)

$\Delta f_{sk} = 100$ N/mm^2 (wires in sheath)

Tendons

(a) *48 wires of 6 mm dia.*
        $A_p = 1357$ mm^2
        Sheath dia. 66 mm
(b) *32 wires of 6 mm dia.*
        $A_p = 905$ mm^2
        Sheath dia. 61 mm

For (a) and (b)

Friction coefficient 0·16
Wobble 0·005 m^{-1}
No wedge slip

B2.3. Loading conditions
Formwork between two girders   1·5 kN/m
Parapet barriers, median barrier, etc.   30 kN/m
Surfacing 10 cm, weight 24 kN/m^3
Live loads according to Appendix 1 of FIP recommendations (type H1, heavy).

Table B1. Concrete   2.1

	Precast		In situ, 28 days	
	3 days	28 days		
Compressive strength, f_{ck}: N/mm^2	20	40	30	Fig
Tensile strength, f_{ctm}: N/mm^2	2·2	3·4	2·8	Fig
E-modulus, E_{cm}: kN/mm^2	29	35	32	Fig
Shrinkage, $\varepsilon_{cs}(t_\infty, t_0) \times 10^3$	0·26	0·23	0·23	Tab
Creep, $\varphi(t_\infty, t_0)$	2·7	2·2	2·2	Tab

Table B2. Reinforcing steel (high bond)   2.2

	Bars	Fabrics
Strength, f_{yk}: N/mm^2	400	500
E-modulus, E_s: kN/mm^2	200	200
Fatigue strength, Δf_{sk}: N/mm^2	150	60

Table B3. Prestressing steel   2.3

	Strands	Wires	
Characteristic strength, $f_{0 \cdot 1k}$: N/mm^2	1580	1540	
Tensile strength, f_{tk}: N/mm^2	1820	1770	
Relaxation (final values): %	6	6	
E-modulus, E_s: kN/mm^2	200	200	Fig
Fatigue strength, Δf_{sk}: N/mm^2	150	100	

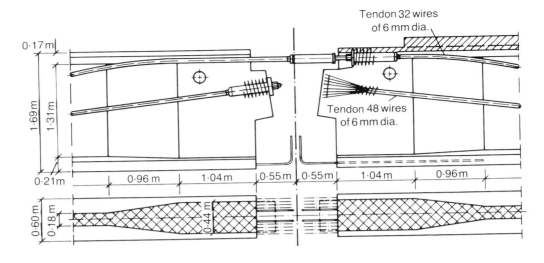

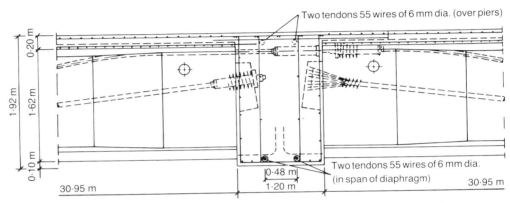

Fig. B6. Support detail of precast girders (before and after casting of diaphragm)

B2.4. Serviceability conditions
(Relative humidity $\approx 75\%$.)
Concrete cover 30 mm

Permanent loading: fully prestressed $\left.\right\}$ requirements

Full loading: $\sigma_s \leqslant 200$ N/mm^2, $\Delta\sigma_p \leqslant 200$ N/mm$^2 \left.\right\}$ from client

Deflection limit $\left.\right\}$ no requirements

Crack limit $\left.\right\}$ from client

B. Basic data

B3.1. Materials
Concrete, see Table B1.
Reinforcing steel, see Table B2.
Prestressing steel, see Table B3.

B3.2. Loads
Dead load for one beam
For section areas see Table B12.

Girder	$g_0 = 0.53 \times 25$	$= 13.3$ kN/m	*2.1.6*
Girder + slab	$g_1 = 1.19 \times 25$	$= 29.8$ kN/m	
Barriers (full distribution)	$g_2 = (1/6) \times 30$	$= 5.0$ kN/m	
Surfacing	$g_3 = 3.80 \times 0.1 \times 24$	$= \underline{9.2}$ kN/m	
	Total g	$= \overline{44.0}$ kN/m	

Live load (normal traffic loading) *App. 1*
Uniformly distributed load (heavy) *Fig. A1*

12 kN/m² for serviceability limit state (loaded length 0·6l)
9·8 kN/m² for ultimate limit state (loaded length 2l)

Three lanes per direction: reductions to 75% or 50%
Concentrated load (heavy) 400 kN

Fig. ₁
A1.1..

B3.3. Position of reinforcement
At midspan
Strands 50 mm from bottom.
First tendon 70 mm from bottom.
Second tendon 170 mm from bottom.
Mild steel

at top 1780 mm from bottom
at bottom 70 mm from bottom.

At support (for continuity between girders)
Second tendon 1550 mm from bottom.
Mild steel 1550 mm from bottom.

B4. Prestressing

B4.1. At the moment of tensioning
Eight strands

$0.90 \times 1580 = 1422$ N/mm²

$0.80 \times 1820 = 1456$ N/mm²

1422 < 1456

$P_i = 744 \times 1422 \times 10^{-3} = 1058$ kN

Tendons

$0.90 \times 1540 = 1386$ N/mm²

$0.80 \times 1770 = 1416$ N/mm²

1386 < 1416

48 wires of 6 mm dia.

$P_i = 1357 \times 1386 \times 10^{-3} = 1882$ kN

32 wires of 6 mm dia.

$P_i = 905 \times 1386 \times 10^{-3} = 1254$ kN

3.2.1(

B4.2. Initial prestress after transfer
Eight strands

$0.85 \times 1580 = 1343$ N/mm²

$0.75 \times 1820 = 1365$ N/mm²

3.2.1(

Table B4. Losses due to friction

Tendon	x	α	$\Delta\alpha = kx$	$\dfrac{\Delta P_i}{P_i}$	P: kN		After de-tensionin
					Tensioning	De-tensioning	
48 wires of	0	0	0	0	1842	1712	$P_{max} = 1777$ kN =
6 mm dia.	$l/2$	0·143	0·079	0·04	1777	**1777**	
	l	0·286	0·157	0·07	1712	1712	
32 wires of	0	0	0	0	1254	1072	$P_{max} = 1163$ kN $<$
6 mm dia.	2·00 m	0·188	0·010	0·03	1214	1112	
	$l/2$	0·376	0·077	0·07	1163	**1163**	
	$l - 2.00$ m	0·564	0·145	0·11	1112	1112	
	l	0·752	0·155	0·15	1072	1072	

$$1343 < 1365$$
$$P_0 = 744 \times 1343 \times 10^{-3} = 1000 \text{ kN}$$

Tendons

$$0.85 \times 1540 = 1309 \text{ N/mm}^2$$
$$0.75 \times 1770 = 1328 \text{ N/mm}^2$$
$$\mathbf{1309} < 1328$$

48 wires of 6 mm dia.

$$P_0 = 1357 \times 1309 \times 10^{-3} = 1777 \text{ kN}$$

32 wires of 6 mm dia.

$$P_0 = 905 \times 1309 \times 10^{-3} = 1185 \text{ kN}$$

B4.3. Immediate losses

3.3.2

Eight strands: instantaneous concrete deformation

$$\Delta P = \alpha \sigma_{\text{cpi}} A_{\text{p}} = 7 \times 6.3 \times 744 = 33 \text{ kN}$$

$$\sigma_{\text{cpi}}^{(-)} = \frac{1.058}{0.53} + \frac{1.058 \times 0.89}{0.219} = 6.3 \text{ N/mm}^2$$

(values from Table B12)

$$P_0 = 1058 - 33 = 1025 \approx 1000 \text{ kN}$$

(elastic deformation due to tendons neglected).

Losses due to friction

$$\frac{\Delta P_{\text{i}}}{P_{\text{i}}} = \mu(\alpha + kx)$$

$$P = \left(1 - \frac{\Delta P_{\text{i}}}{P_{\text{i}}}\right)P_{\text{i}}$$

See Table B4.

B4.4. Estimation of time-dependent losses

B4.4.1. Construction programme
See Table B5.

B4.4.2. Losses due to creep at l/2
(Stresses σ_{cpm} from Fig. B9.)

Strands + first tendon

3 days gives $\varphi_\infty = 2.7$.

See Table B6.

$$\Delta\sigma_{\text{p}}^{(-)} = 67 \text{ N/mm}^2 \text{ gives loss of prestress } \sim 5\%.$$

Table B5. Construction programme

	Time, t
Casting girder	0
Tensioning (strands + first tendon)	3 days
Placed in final position	28 days
Concreting of slab	42 days
Tensioning of second tendon	56 days
Surfacing	90 days

Second tendon

56 days gives $\varphi_\infty = 2\cdot2$.

See Table B7.

$\Delta\sigma_p^{(-)} = 22$ N/mm^2 gives loss of prestress $\sim 2\%$.

B4.4.3. Losses due to shrinkage
Strands + first tendon

$0\cdot26 \times 200 = 52$ N/mm$^2 = \sim 4\%$

Second tendon

$0\cdot23 \times 200 = 46$ N/mm$^2 = \sim 4\%$

Table B6. Losses due to creep at l/2: strands + first tendon (stresses in N/mm^2)   Fig. 2.5

Period: days	$\dfrac{\Delta\varphi}{\varphi_\infty}$	$\sigma_{cpm}^{(-)}$	$\Delta\sigma_p^{(-)} \approx \Delta\varphi\alpha\sigma_{cpm}$
0–28	35%	7	46
28–56	15%	~ 0	—
56–90	10%	4	7
90–∞	40%	2	14
Total	—	—	67

Table B7. Losses due to creep at l/2: second tendon (stresses in N/mm^2)   Fig. 2.5

Period: days	$\dfrac{\Delta\varphi}{\varphi_\infty}$	$\sigma_{cpm}^{(-)}$	$\Delta\sigma_p^{(-)} \approx \Delta\varphi\alpha\sigma_{cpm}$
56–90	40%	4	22
90–∞	60%	~ 0	—
Total	—	—	22

Table B8. Prestressing forces (kN)

	At midspan			At supports		
	P_0	P_{56}	P_∞	P_0	P_{56}	P_∞
Strands	−1000	−930	−880	−1000	−910	−8
First tendon	−1777	−1653	−1564	−1712	−1558	−14
Second tendon	—	−1163	−1058	—	−1072	−9

Table B9. Isostatic prestressing moments (kN m)

	At midspan			At supports		
	M_{p0}	M_{p56}	$M_{p\infty}$	M_{p0}	M_{p56}	$M_{p\infty}$
Strands	−890	−828	−783	−870	−792	−748
First tendon	−1546	−1438	−1361	—	—	—
Second tendon	—	−1396	−1270	—	300	273

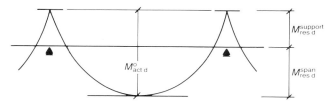

Fig. B7. Moment distribution according to the statical method of the theory of plasticity

B4.4.4. Total losses
(Includes reduced relaxation: 5% instead of 6%)   *Fig. 2.8*

Strands + first tendon

  $5 + 4 + 5 = 14\%$ gives 12%

Second tendon

  $2 + 4 + 5 = 11\%$ gives 9%

Values obtained by superposition may be divided by approximately   *3.3.3*

$$1 - 6 \times \frac{(-18)}{1300} \times \left(1 + \frac{2\cdot7}{2}\right) = 1\cdot20$$

B4.4.5. Partial losses (after 56 days)
Strands + first tendon   *Fig. 2.5*
                                                                           Fig. 2.8

  $(4\cdot5 + 2 + 2) \times \dfrac{1}{1\cdot2}$ gives 7%

B4.5. Prestressing forces and isostatic moments   *3.4.2*
(See sections B3.3 and Table B12.)

Prestressing forces are shown in Table B8, and moments in Table B9.

5. Ultimate limit ate design

B5.1. Principle (static method of the theory of plasticity)   *4.2.2*
Load distribution in transverse direction assumed to be constant (ductility of slab to be checked). Moment distribution in longitudinal direction: see Fig. B7.   *Fig. 4.2*

Condition to be fulfilled

  $M^{\mathrm{o}}_{\mathrm{act\,d}} \leqslant M^{\mathrm{support}}_{\mathrm{res\,d}} + M^{\mathrm{span}}_{\mathrm{res\,d}}$ *1.2*

with

  $M^{\mathrm{o}}_{\mathrm{act\,d}} = M(1\cdot35g;\ 1\cdot5q)$ *4.1.2*

  $M_{\mathrm{res\,d}} = M(0\cdot8f_{\mathrm{ck}}/1\cdot5;\ f_{\mathrm{yk}}/1\cdot15;\ f_{0\cdot1\mathrm{k}}/1\cdot15)$ *4.1.3*
                                                                           Fig. 4.4
                                                                           Fig. 2.6
Ductility condition   *Fig. 2.9*
                                                                           4.3.2
  $\rho_{\mathrm{id}} \leqslant 0\cdot02$ *4.2.4*

Mechanical degree of prestressing: λ.   *3.1.2*
                                                                           3.4.3(d)

B5.2. Determination of acting moment $M^{\mathrm{o}}_{\mathrm{act\,d}}$ (for final stage)
Dead load from section B3.2

  $g = 44\cdot0$ kN/m

Ultimate limit state gives

$$M_{gd}^o = 1.35 \times 44 \times \frac{32.15^2}{8} = 7670 \text{ kN m}$$

Uniformly distributed load (see section B3.2)

2 lanes: $q_1 = 9.8 \times 7.5$ $= 73.5$ kN/m
2 lanes: $q_2 = 0.75 \times 9.8 \times 7.5$ $= 55.1$ kN/m
2 lanes: $q_3 = 0.50 \times 9.8 \times 7.5$ $= 36.8$ kN/m
Total for six beams: q $= 165.4$ kN/m
For one beam: q $= 27.6$ kN/m

Ultimate limit state gives

$$M_{qd}^o = 1.5 \times 27.6 \times \frac{32.15^2}{8} = 5343 \text{ kN m}$$

Concentrated load: 400 kN

For one beam: $Q = 67$ kN

Ultimate limit state gives

$$M_{Qd}^o = 1.5 \times 67 \times \frac{32.15}{4} = 800 \text{ kN m}$$

$$M_{act\,d}^o = 7670 + 5343 + 800 \approx 13\,810 \text{ kN m}$$

B5.3. Determination of resisting moment $M_{res\,d}^{support}$

Reinforcement tensile forces at ultimate limit state   *Fig. 2.6*
See Table B10 ($\varepsilon_s > \varepsilon_y$ gives $\sigma_s = f_y$).   *Fig. 2.9*

Concrete compressive force at ultimate limit state   *Fig. 4.4*

$$F_c = 0.8 \times \frac{40}{1.5} \times (600 \times 175 + 180a) \times 10^{-3} = 3650 \text{ kN}$$

Participation of web

$a = 365$ mm

$175 + 365$ corresponds to $0.8x = 540$ mm

Axis of F_c (from bottom)

Table B10. Determination of $M_{res\,d}^{support}$: steel tensile forces at ultimate limit state

	Steel	d: m	A_s: mm²	$f_{sk}/1.15$: N/mm²	F_s: kN
Slab	56 bars of 12 mm dia.	1.78	6330	348	2200
Girder	14 bars of 8 mm dia.	1.55	700	348	240
Tendon	32 wires of 6 mm dia.	1.55	905	1340	1210
					3650

Table B11. Determination of $M_{res\,d}^{span}$: steel tensile forces at ultimate limit state

	Steel	d: m	A_s: mm²	$f_{sk}/1.15$: N/mm²	F_s: kN
Strands	8 strands of 0.5 in dia.	1.77	714	1374	981
Tendon 1	48 wires of 6 mm dia.	1.75	1357	1340	1817
Tendon 2	32 wires of 6 mm dia.	1.65	905	1340	1212
Flange	8 bars of 22 mm dia.	1.65	3040	348	1058
Fabric	10 bars of 6 mm dia.	1.50	283	435	123
					5190

$$b \approx \frac{0.6 \times 0.175 \times 0.09 + 0.18 \times 0.365 \times 0.36}{0.6 \times 0.175 + 0.18 \times 0.365} = 0.19 \text{ m}$$

Resisting moment

$$M = \sum [F_s(d_s - b)]$$

$$M_{\text{res d}}^{\text{support}} = 2200 \times 1.59 + 240 \times 1.36 + 1210 \times 1.36$$

$$= 3500 + 330 + 1650$$

$$= 5480 \text{ kN m}$$

B5.4. Determination of resisting moment $M_{\text{res d}}^{\text{span}}$

Reinforcement tensile forces at ultimate limit state

See Table B11.

Concrete compressive force at ultimate limit state   *Fig. 4.4*

$$F_c = 0.8 \times \frac{30}{1.5} \times 3800a \times 10^{-3} = 5170 \text{ kN} \approx 5190 \text{ kN}$$

$$a = 0.8x = 85 \text{ mm}$$

$$0.4x = 0.04 \text{ m}$$

Resisting moment

$$M = \sum [F_s(d_s - 0.4x)]$$

$$M_{\text{res d}}^{\text{span}} = 981 \times 1.73 + 1817 \times 1.71 + 1212 \times 1.61 + 1058 \times 1.61$$

$$+ 123 \times 1.46$$

$$= 1700 + 3100 + 1950 + 1703 + 180$$

$$= 8630 \text{ kN m}$$

Inner lever arm

$$z = \frac{8630}{5190} = 1.66 \text{ m}$$

B5.5. Checks

(Values from sections B5.2–B5.4)

Equilibrium according to section B5.1

$$13\,810 < 14\,110 = 5480 + 8630$$

Ductility   *4.2.4*

Support

$$\rho_{\text{id}} \approx \frac{1}{600} \times \left(\frac{6330}{1780} + \frac{700}{1550} + \frac{905}{1550} \times \frac{1540}{400} \right) = 0.0104 = 1.04\%$$

Span

$$\rho_{\text{id}} = \frac{1}{3800} \left[\frac{283}{1500} \times \frac{500}{400} + \frac{3040}{1650} + \left(\frac{905}{1650} + \frac{1357}{1750} \right) \times \frac{1540}{400} \right.$$

$$\left. + \frac{714}{1770} \times \frac{1580}{400} \right] = 0.0023 = 0.23\%$$

In both cases

$$\rho_{\text{id}} < 0.020$$

There is sufficient reserve for any indirect actions, e.g. support settle-   *4.1.2*
ments.

3.1.2

Mechanical degree of prestressing (for information)

Support

$$\lambda = \frac{1210}{3650} = 0.33$$

or

$$\lambda = \frac{1650}{5480} = 0.30$$

Span

$$\lambda = \frac{4010}{5190} = 0.77$$

or

$$\lambda = \frac{6750}{8630} = 0.78$$

(based on resisting forces or resisting moments).

B5.6. Shear in web

4.4.2

The calculation for shear in web is not given here. In relevant cases, the FIP recommendations should be followed (see Example A).

Table B12. Cross-sectional values (including bonded reinforcement)

	In span		At support (0·55 m from support centre)	
	Girder	Final section	Girder	Final section
Section area: m²	0·53	1·19	0·88	1·53
Centre (from bottom): m	0·94	1·37	0·92	1·27
Moment of inertia: m⁴	0·195	0·395	0·253	0·503
Moduli of inertia: m³				
Slab top	—	0·878	—	0·915
Girder top	0·260	1·234	0·329	1·198
Girder strands	0·219	—	—	—
Bottom	0·207	0·288	0·275	0·396

Table B13. Bending moments

	Load: kN/m	Bending moments: kN m	
		Support	Midspan
Girder only	13·3	—	1722
Formwork slab	1·5	—	194
Formwork slab	−1·5	+104	−143
In situ slab	16·5	—	2132
Barriers	5·0	−446	223
Surfacing	9·2	−787	393
Traffic*	$(q + Q)_{max}$	−2240	2450
Traffic*	$(q + Q)_{min}$	+630	−920
Prestressing	Isostatic	—†	—†
Tendon 2	Hyperstatic$_0$	+412	+206
Tendon 2	Hyperstatic$_\infty$	+267	+267

* For infrequent loading.
† See Table B9.

Table 5.

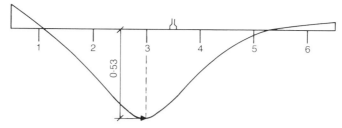

Fig. B8. Influence line for reaction taken by beam 3

B5.7. Web–flange connection
The calculation for the web–flange connection is not given here. In relevant cases, the FIP recommendations should be followed (see Example A).

4.4.3

B5.8. Fatigue (stresses from Fig. B10)
The calculation for fatigue is not given here. In relevant cases, the FIP recommendations should be followed (see Example F).

4.8

B5.9. Ultimate limit state for construction phase (simply supported beam)
From section B5.4

$$M_{\text{res d}} \approx (8630 - 1950) \times \frac{1 \cdot 54}{1 \cdot 66} = 6200 \text{ kN m}$$

(no participation of tendon 2 or deck slab).

From Table B13

$$M_{\text{act}} = 1722 + 194 + 2132 = 4050 \text{ kN m}$$

Partial safety coefficient

$$\gamma_g = \frac{6200}{4050} = 1 \cdot 53 > 1 \cdot 35 \text{ (OK)}$$

. Serviceability limit state checks including construction phase)

B6.1. Cross-sectional values
See Table B12.

B6.2. Structural analysis (elasticity theory)
Transverse distribution
Influence lines determined by classical method based on elastic behaviour; for beam 3 see Fig. B8.

Bending moments
See Table B13.

Redistribution due to change of statical system (creep)
For results see Fig. B9.

5.2.2

Redistribution due to different concrete ages between girder and slab (shrinkage + creep)
For results see Fig. B9.

Possible support settlement of 15 mm
Application of elasticity theory and reduction to 30% (favourable creep effect on stresses due to slow displacement of long duration) results in

$$\pm 0 \cdot 5 \text{ N/mm}^2 \text{ at top}$$

and

$\mp 1 \cdot 1$ N/mm^2 at bottom

(not presented in section B6.3.1).

B6.3. Concrete and steel stresses

B6.3.1. Uncracked state
See Fig. B9.

Check of redistribution effect at midspan by approximation   5.2.2

From section B4.5 and Table B13

$$M_0 = 3854 - 2903 = 951 \text{ kN m}$$

In one-mass system

$$M_e \approx 3854 \times \frac{0 \cdot 042}{0 \cdot 125} - 480 = 816 \text{ kN m}$$

$$M_\infty = 951 + (816 - 951) \times \frac{2 \cdot 2}{3 \cdot 2} = 858 \text{ kN m}$$

Bottom

$$\sigma_e = \frac{858}{0 \cdot 288} \times 10^{-3} = 3 \cdot 0 \text{ N/mm}^2$$

To be compared with

$$\sigma = \sigma_0 - 1 \cdot 1 = \frac{951}{207} - 1 \cdot 1 = 3 \cdot 5 \text{ N/mm}^2$$

(same order of magnitude).

B6.3.2. Cracked state
See Fig. B10.

B6.3.3. Stress limits

$\sigma_{cc} \leqslant 0 \cdot 5 f_{ck} = 10$ or 20 or 15 N/mm^2 always satisfied   5.3.1

$\sigma_s^{\parallel}$ and $\Delta \sigma_p^{\parallel} \leqslant 200$ N/mm^2 (see section B2.4)

Permanent loading

$$\sigma_{c \max} = 0 \cdot 6 \text{ N/mm}^2 > 0$$

Small excess may be tolerated, because favourable effect of creep (redistribution) starts earlier than taken into account in calculation.

Criterion for limited prestress   3.4.3

$$\sigma_{ct} \leqslant 0 \cdot 75 f_{ctk} = 0 \cdot 75 \times (1 \cdot 7 \text{ or } 2 \cdot 7 \text{ or } 2 \cdot 2)$$ Fig. 5.2

Under full loading not satisfied; gives partial prestressing (see section B6.5).

B6.3.4. Principal tensile stresses in the web   3.4.3
The calculation for principal tensile stresses in the web is not applicable here. In relevant cases, the FIP recommendations should be followed.

B6.4. Deformations   5.4
Under permanent loading, deflection is small (dead load almost balanced by prestressing).

Under live load in midspan

$$a_{\max} = 15 \text{ mm}$$

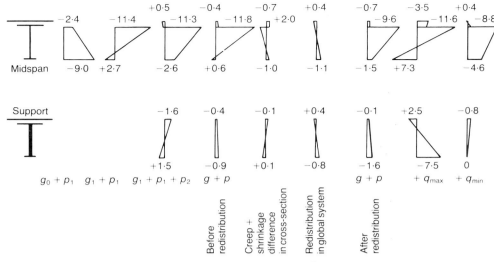

Fig. B9. Concrete stresses, uncracked state (N/mm^2)

(a)   (b)

Fig. B10. Concrete and steel stresses for critical section—midspan under $g + p + q_{max}$ (infrequent loading) (N/mm^2): (a) uncracked state; (b) cracked state

(calculation based on elasticity theory, later confirmed by load test on erected bridge).

Values for comparison

$$\frac{a}{l} = \frac{15}{32\,150} = \frac{1}{2140}$$

slenderness

$$\frac{l}{h} = \frac{32 \cdot 15}{1 \cdot 82} = 18$$

B6.5. Crack control
Frequent traffic action   *5.5.5*

$\psi_1 \approx 0.6$ *Table 5.1*

$\sigma_s \approx 155 \text{ N/mm}^2$

(under $g + p + 0.6q$)

$h_{ef}/h_t \approx 0$

Gives $s_{max} = 100$ mm.   *Fig. 5.4*

$h_{ef}/h_t \approx 0$

(flange) $s \approx 50$ mm

Gives $\rho_{min} = 0.3\%$.   *Fig. 5.5*

(flange) $A_{c\,ef} = 600 \times 175 = 105\,000 \text{ mm}^2$

$A_{s\,min} = 1050 \times 0.3 = 315 \text{ mm}^2$

(largely satisfied, taking into account strands and ordinary reinforcement).

B7. Detailing

See Figs B4 and B6.

6

ample C   Kotka Bridge, Finland: five-span box girder road bridge

Incremental launching method

Example prepared by S. Rantanen (Espoo), with the assistance of C. Feyereisen (Lausanne), H. R. Ganz (Berne), W. Koehler (Vienna) and B. Westerberg (Stockholm)

References to *FIP recommendations: Practical design of reinforced and prestressed concrete structures (based on the CEB–FIP model code (MC78))* are given in the right-hand margin

**Incremental
ıching method**

C1.1. Introduction

The basic idea of the incremental launching method (ILM) is simple. In stationary formwork, located usually behind an abutment, a short segment of the bridge is cast and prestressed against the identical segments already cast. Then the formwork is released by being lowered slightly and the bridge is moved by the length of a segment. The structure slides on temporary sliding bearings situated on abutments and piers. This procedure is repeated until the whole structure is in its final position. During launching, the concrete beam is provided with a special steel nose in order to reduce the cantilever moment.

This method thus differs from the free cantilever method, where the formwork moves.

Due to the special actions during launching, the quantity of longitudinal prestressing material in an incrementally launched bridge is greater than in a cast in situ bridge. The longitudinal prestress is applied in two stages. During launching there is only the 'centrical' prestress, which consists of the straight tendons, usually in the top and bottom flanges of the girder.

The method also demands special equipment, such as the launching nose, jacks, sliding bearings, friction bearings, side guidance etc. After launching, the bridge has to be lifted so that the temporary sliding bearings can be taken out and the final bearings installed.

There are, of course, economic advantages in applying the incremental launching method. Since the early 1960s, it has been a competitive construction method for continuous medium-span concrete bridges.

C1.2. Advantages and disadvantages

C1.2.1. Advantages

Economy

The most significant advantage to all those who use the incremental launching method and have thus invested in the special equipment required is the fact that most continuous concrete beam bridges can be built with this method. A typical incrementally launched bridge has several spans of 30–60 m. If the spans are greater, the method is still possible but temporary piers are needed.

In the 1970s it was considered that the minimum length at which an incrementally launched bridge could be economically viable was about 200 m. Nowadays the method is applied to bridges of length less than 100 m. This is due to a fact which is independent of the bridge length and the number of formwork circuits; i.e. the minimum disturbance to the area beneath the bridge (once the piers have been built). This is particularly important when the bridge crosses motorways, railways or canals. The costs of traffic guidance and possible accidents can thus be avoided.

From the contractor's point of view, one main advantage is the possibility of high-grade industrialization of the construction work. The formwork site can be an easily accessible area, for instance behind an abutment. All the construction activities are then concentrated in that one place. Because the formwork is usually relatively short (i.e. 15–30 m), it can be easily sheltered so that work can continue despite wind and rain. In cold countries the shelter can be heated, and the temperature of the segment can be kept above $+5°C$ until the cables have been injected.

Working according to a weekly sequence in order to manufacture one segment makes work faster and lowers costs. A structure achieved in this way is usually very accurate. Compared with casting in situ and with precast construction, the advantages of the incremental launching method become dominant when the costs of the falsework are significant. This may be the case when the bridge is situated at a high level or over soft ground where heavy lifting machines have difficulties of access.

Safety

During launching, every point of the bridge has to pass over sliding bearings. Consequently every cross-section is affected by bending moments of reverse direction and therefore only uniform prestress is possible. The common way to produce this is to locate straight tendons in the top and bottom flanges of the beam. Normally these tendons are retained to form a part of the final prestress. The other part of the prestress is produced by curved tendons which are installed after launching.

Because of the straight tendons, an incrementally launched bridge has significantly more prestress than a cast in situ bridge. Although this makes the solution less economic, the straight tendons ensure an exceptionally safe, durable and maintenance-free structure. The reserve of safety can be significant for bridges in earthquake regions and soft ground. However, it is difficult to estimate the value of these benefits in economic terms, and it is not known if they have influenced the choice of construction method in any particular case.

C1.2.2. Disadvantages

Appearance

The most frequently mentioned disadvantage of an incrementally launched bridge is its ungraceful appearance. This is mainly due to the span-to-depth ratio of the girder, which is normally 15–18, whereas for a cast in situ bridge a value of 22 or more is quite usual.

As the formwork is used several times, it may suffer slight damage, which may affect the visible surfaces of the bridge.

The changes in concrete (or cement) during the long construction period may also affect the colour of the structure.

Soffit

The soffit must be regular for the whole length of the bridge; i.e. a straight line, or a straight line in the vertical or horizontal plane and a circular arc in the other. Deviations from these basic cases are to some extent possible, but they are expensive. For example, combined horizontal and vertical curvature can be achieved by inclining the plane in which the circular arc lies. If the road has an S shape, the girder can be launched from both abutments and then joined in the middle with in situ concrete, etc. Nowadays the trend is to apply the incremental launching method in more and more geometrically complex bridges, and astonishingly difficult cases have been solved. Variations in the bridge width can to some extent be solved by varying only the width of the deck-slab cantilevers. In limited crossings (a low passage etc.) the required structural depth may sometimes prevent the use of the incremental launching method.

Working space

In general, working space is not a relevant factor: normally there is enough space behind the abutments on the road or railway line. In some special cases where problems have arisen, the solution has often been to use very short formwork. Segments of only a few metres have been used.

Economy

Costs are increased by the high material consumption, the multiphase prestressing and injection work needed, and the high degree of accuracy required. Thus in normal circumstances a cast in situ or precast beam bridge is cheaper than an incrementally launched one. The incremental launching method becomes competitive only in particular circumstances. It is difficult to make comparisons because of different norms, traditions, equipment available and relative labour to material costs in different countries.

C1.3. Design

C1.3.1. Loadings

During launching, the loading consists normally only of the self-weight of the girder and the launching nose. Usually cornices and even cross-girders are added after the launching process.

Using stainless steel sliding surfaces and Teflon-covered rubber bearings with lubrication keeps the friction small (only 1–2%), and the girder moves smoothly without any vibration. Only mishandling or the rupture of a bearing affects the structure. In design, the use of an impact coefficient is recommended to take account of this. At the front of the girder, wind can cause vibrations to the steel nose, so the impact coefficient may be increased there. Friction in sliding bearings must be considered in pier design.

In the example, impact coefficients 1·05 and 1·10 are used. In some countries impact is not taken into account, but instead a working load of 0·75 kN/m is applied on the deck.

Differential support settlements appear from soil compression and compression of the piers, which may be of different heights. Also, the tolerances on bearing levels have to be taken into consideration. The support settlement is considered to be a short term phenomenon. When the sliding bearings are replaced by the final bearings, the effects of these settlements can be cancelled.

The temperature difference between the top and bottom flanges is usually taken as 10°C; but, because this can have a strong influence on crack formation, the temperature of the structure is sometimes controlled and lower values are accepted. Even a value of 2·5°C has been used.

A particular action during launching derives from the level tolerances of the sliding bearings and from the deviation tolerances of the cross-sectional dimensions of the girder. Usually the tolerances are fixed before design is started. The girder and the bearings are then controlled to comply with these values.

An accuracy of ±1 mm is often demanded for the sliding surfaces. The dimensions of the cross-section are normally allowed to vary by ±5 mm. The configuration of a typical casting area, with production concentrated in one area, facilitates achievement of accuracy, work supervision and hence also quality of workmanship. Tolerance requirements are normally satisfied without difficulty.

C1.3.2. Action effects

The stresses due to action effects during launching should be calculated for every launching stage by the theory of elasticity. The different stiffnesses of the launching nose and the piers must be taken into account.

Torsion and the distribution of reactions to adjacent bearings are computed according to the fixed tolerances.

Except for the first span behind the steel nose, these calculations normally show that action effects (max./min.) are almost constant for the rest of the launched girder.

C1.3.3. Time-dependent effects

The analysis of the time-dependent effects in a staged segmentally constructed prestressed concrete girder is a complex and laborious design procedure. The effects which have to be taken into account are prestress, concrete ageing, creep, shrinkage and steel relaxation. These effects must be timed according to the construction timetable.

After launching, the curved tendons are added, which also complicates the analysis.

As this can be a time-consuming analysis, it is recommended that appropriate computer programs are used. These have already been developed by some designers.[1]

For preliminary estimation, the losses in tendons can be calculated with mean design values and coefficients on the safe side. This is quite important because it is necessary to have an idea about the prestress needed during launching and in the final structure. The dimensions of the cross-section can depend on the number of straight tendons etc.

C1.3.4. Serviceability limit state

As mentioned previously, the girder has to be relatively deep because of the bending moments during launching. Particular attention must be paid to the efficiency of the cross-section. It can be estimated[2] from the value of ρ

$$\rho = \frac{I_c}{A_c(h - y_c)y_c}$$

The value of ρ should be as large as is practically possible. The use of a box cross-section with relatively thin webs is very appropriate to fulfil this condition. In reality, however, the web width is controlled by local effects due to the sliding bearings, the resistance against shear and also the practical rules of casting concrete. In a box section an efficiency value of more than 0·50 is easily reached, and even a value of $\rho = 0·55$ is not unusual. A T-section is clearly less advantageous: the value of ρ hardly ever reaches 0·45. A flat slab is the most inefficient of practical cross-sections: the value of ρ is only about 0·33.

The box cross-section of a road bridge has appeared to be particularly advantageous if it has wide side cantilevers for the road slab. Then the ratio between the top and bottom section moduli is similar to the ratio of hogging and sagging moments affecting the section during launching. Consequently the required centrical prestress is about equal for the two bending directions. In railway bridges, a wide top slab is rarely required and so the ratio becomes less advantageous and more prestress is needed during launching.

A T-section demands still more centrical prestress, but such a section is sometimes justified for short-span bridges because of the relatively low cost of formwork. A rectangular or slab section is not recommended in general for an incrementally launched girder. The centrical prestress needed during launching consists normally of straight tendons located and anchored in top and bottom flanges.

The prestress force must be such that only moderate stresses occur in the concrete during launching. For compressive stress, the limit which is usually allowed is about $0·5 f_{ck}$. Taking into account the tendency of young concrete to creep, one can take even more moderate values, for example $0·3f_{ck}$.

Overstepping the tensile strength of the concrete leads to cracks along the whole girder. Thus the structure should preferably remain in compression. If, however, tension is allowed, it should not exceed the values given in the FIP recommendations. It is also recommended that crack width is estimated on the assumption that concrete does not resist tension at all.

C1.3.5. Ultimate limit state

In proceeding to the ultimate limit state calculations in the launching stage, the empty ducts of the curved tendons must be taken into account. When they are situated in the top or bottom flange they diminish the concrete compressive area, and when situated in the webs they diminish the shear capacity of the girder.

The straight tendons should preferably be injected immediately so that they can work efficiently in bending. If for any reason the injection is delayed, the tendons have to be treated as unbonded tendons in calculations.

The role of the tendons in the concrete compressive zone is open to discussion. The decrease of their prestressing force has to be taken into account according to the shortening of the adjacent concrete. If this strain is around 0.35%, the prestress practically vanishes. But during launching the strain is usually significantly smaller and a great deal of the prestress remains. What safety coefficient should be applied to this force? A solution on the safe side is to consider this force as a permanent load and use the same safety coefficient as for the dead load.

The structure is sufficiently ductile during launching because at this stage only relatively few tendons are in use. At the final stage, when the curved tendons also are prestressed, the situation is less advantageous. In section 4.2.4 of the recommendations, no exact rules are given for the increase of concrete compressive strain due to the stirrups and longitudinal reinforcement used on the compression side of the cross-section.

C1.3.6. Detailing

When a check is made on the effects of local forces during launching, it should be remembered that they act on young concrete whose tensile strength is still relatively low. The risk of crack formation is thus greater than usual, and the amount and spacing of reinforcement should take account of this.

During launching, the local force effects are mainly due to the anchorages of the straight tendons and the bearing reactions.

Fig. C1. Kotka Bridge

The sliding bearings should be as large as possible, although the piers then have a rather massive appearance.

If a large bevel is used in the girder, the sliding bearings cannot operate too near corners and the pressure is spread more smoothly to the horizontal cross-section of the web.

C1.4. Design example
Kotka Bridge (Fig. C1) is a five-span road bridge 225 m long which was constructed in 1983 by the incremental launching method.

In its final stage the bridge is a normal continuous girder bridge. Only the particular loading cases and design questions concerning the launching stage are highlighted in the example.

C2. Design data

C2.1. Intended use and materials
Road bridge, $L = 5 \times 45 = 225$ m.
Concrete: C40 (normally hardening cement is used).
Reinforcement: S400 (deformed bars, high bond).
Prestressing steel: S1420/1570 ($f_{0.2k}/f_{tk}$), 12·2 mm dia., $f_{0.1k} = 1220$ MN/m^2.

C2.2. Loading conditions
Permanent loads
Dead weight of box girder: $g_0 = 180.0$ kN/m
  Surfacing + edge beams: $g_1 = 58.0$ kN/m
  Far distance heating water tubes (inside the box): $g_2 = 11.9$ kN/m
(g_1 and g_2 are applied after launching.)

Live loads (client's requirements)
Traffic load

  $q = 3.0$ kN/m^2 on two lanes of 3·0 m

  $Q = 3 \times 210$ kN on two lanes of 3·0 m

Pedestrian load

  $q = 4.0$ kN/m^2 without traffic load

  $q = 2.0$ kN/m^2 with traffic load

Temperature
Temperature difference between the deck and bottom slab $+10°$C/$-5°$C.

Special loading conditions during launching
Steel nose ($M = 4.04$ MN m, $V = 0.34$ MN) in front of the concrete girder to reduce cantilever moment.

  Dead weight $g_0 = 180.0$ kN/m; impact coefficient 1·10 in the front part and 1·05 otherwise.

  Temperature difference $+2.5°$C between deck and bottom slab (to be controlled during the work).

  Settling of piers 10 mm (short term phenomenon).

  Tolerances of the work: level of the sliding bearings, ± 1 mm; dimensions of concrete box girders, ± 5 mm (especially the height differences of adjacent corners).

  The total difference in the levels of the sliding bearings is thus taken as $1 + 1 + 5 = 7$ mm (Fig. C2). This settling is considered to exist in a group of three successive pairs of sliding bearings (Fig. C3).

C2.3. Serviceability conditions (client's requirements)
No decompression under 'long term load' (= permanent load + 30% of the live load).
  Cracking: $w_k \leqslant 0.1$ mm under total load.

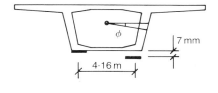

Fig. C2

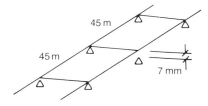

Fig. C3

During launching

Moderate compressive stresses ($\sigma_{cc} < \frac{1}{3} f_{ck}$).

Tensile stresses in concrete sufficiently small that the structure remains theoretically uncracked.

Assuming cracking, $w_k \leqslant 0.15$ mm in both bending directions (i.e. in deck slab and in bottom slab).

C2.4. Materials

Concrete

C40   *2.1.1*

Characteristic strength   *2.1.2*

$$f_{ck} = 40 \text{ MN/m}^2$$

Design strength   *4.1.3*

$$f_{cd} = \frac{f_{ck}}{\gamma_c} = \frac{40}{1 \cdot 5} = 26 \cdot 7 \text{ MN/m}^2$$

Modulus of longitudinal deformation   *2.1.5*

$$E_c = 35\,000 \text{ MN/m}^2$$

$$G_c = 0 \cdot 432 \times 35\,000 = 15\,000 \text{ MN/m}^2$$

Shrinkage and creep   *2.1.7*

Relative humidity 75% (over the sea)

$$\frac{2A_c}{u} = \frac{2 \times 7 \cdot 352}{43} = 0 \cdot 34 \text{ m (box ventilated)}$$

medium $\varepsilon_{cs}(t_\infty, t_0) = 0 \cdot 22 \times 10^{-3}$ *Table 2.1*

mature $\varepsilon_{cs}(t_\infty, t_0) = 0 \cdot 18 \times 10^{-3}$

medium $\varphi(t_\infty, t_0) = 2 \cdot 1$ *Table 2.1*

mature $\varphi(t_\infty, t_0) = 1 \cdot 6$

Launching period: 0·5 year = 180 days   *Fig. 2.5*

$$\frac{\varphi_t}{\varphi_\infty} = 0 \cdot 55$$

$$\frac{\varepsilon_{cst}}{\varepsilon_{cs}} = 0 \cdot 55$$

The development of shrinkage is also estimated from Fig. 2.5 because no other information on that concrete deformation is given in the recommendations.

In this example only the launching period is dealt with. A straight tendon has an anchorage in every second joint; only half of them are prestressed at the same time. Medium values (>7 days) are thus justified. The curved tendons are prestressed after launching (>180 days) and mature values are used for them.

2.2

Reinforcing steel
S400, high bond.
Characteristic strength

$$f_{yk} = 400 \text{ MN/m}^2$$

4.1.3

Design strength

$$f_{yd} = \frac{400}{1 \cdot 15} = 348 \text{ MN/m}^2$$

Modulus of longitudinal deformation

$$E_s = 200\,000 \text{ MN/m}^2$$

In short-term loading

$$\alpha = \frac{E_s}{E_c} = \frac{200}{35} = 5 \cdot 7$$

2.3

Prestressing steel
Prestressing bars 12·2 mm dia., S1420/1570 S($f_{0 \cdot 2k}/f_{tk}$)
Characteristic strength

2.3.1

$$f_{0 \cdot 1k} = 1220 \text{ MN/m}^2$$

Design strength

2.3.4
4.1.3

$$f_{pd} = \frac{1220}{1 \cdot 15} = 1061 \text{ MN/m}^2$$

Modulus of longitudinal deformation (from approval document)

2.3.5

$$E_p = 205\,000 \text{ N/m}^2$$

Initial tendon force (12 bars)

3.2.1

$$\sigma_{p0} = \begin{cases} 0 \cdot 75 \times 1570 = 1177 \text{ MN/m}^2 \\ 0 \cdot 85 \times 1220 = 1037 \text{ MN/m}^2 \end{cases}$$

$$A_p = 12 \times 117 \times 10^{-6} = 1404 \times 10^{-6} \text{ m}^2$$

$$P_0 = 1037 \times 1404 \times 10^{-6} = 1 \cdot 456 \text{ MN}$$

Relaxation

2.3.3
(Fig. 2.

$$\frac{\sigma_{p0}}{f_{tk}} = \frac{1037}{1570} = 0 \cdot 66$$

Relaxation (20°C, 10^3 h, 1037 MPa) < 3% (group 2) (3% according to approval document), see section 3.2.6.4 of MC78.

$$t_2 = 0 \cdot 5 \times 10^6 \text{ h}$$

$$\beta = 0 \cdot 2$$

$$\frac{\Delta\sigma_{prel(2)}}{\Delta\sigma_{prel(1)}} = \left\{\frac{t_2}{t_1}\right\}^\beta = \left\{\frac{0 \cdot 5 \times 10^6}{10^3}\right\}^{0 \cdot 2} = 3 \cdot 47$$

Relaxation (∞) = 3·47 × 3 = 10·4%

Launching time: 6 months = 0·5 year

$$6 \times 30 \times 24 \approx 4 \times 10^3 \text{ h}$$

$$4^{0 \cdot 2} = 1 \cdot 32$$

Relaxation (0·5 year) = 1·32 × 3 = 4·0%

C2.5. Structural summary
See Figs C4–C6.

Fig. C4. System in final phase

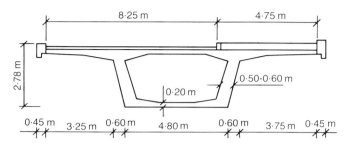

Fig. C5. Cross-section in span

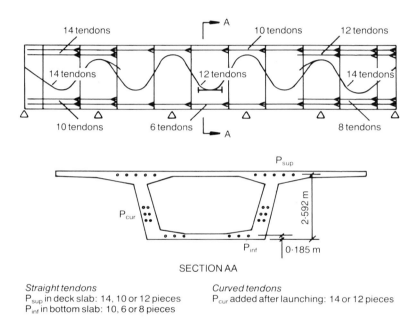

SECTION AA

Straight tendons
P_{sup} in deck slab: 14, 10 or 12 pieces
P_{inf} in bottom slab: 10, 6 or 8 pieces

Curved tendons
P_{cur} added after launching: 14 or 12 pieces

Fig. C6. Prestressing tendons (longitudinal)

3. Cross-section

Only one cross-section in the middle of the central span is discussed in this example. The effective width is

$$b_{ef} = 0{\cdot}60 + 4{\cdot}80 + 0{\cdot}60 + 23/5 = 10{\cdot}60 \text{ m}$$

7.1.4

(Fig. C7), where 23 m is the distance between points of zero moment.

The parts of the deck slab which are inefficient in bending are added to the areas A_c and A_n.

Section data are shown in Table C1.

$$S_c = 3{\cdot}211 \text{ m}^3$$

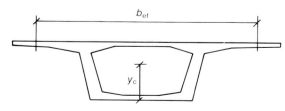

Fig. C7. Cross-section: definitions

Table C1. Section data

	Plain concrete section	Account taken of longitudinal bars and duct holes
A: m^2	7·076	7·352
$h - y_c$: m	1·060	1·060
y_c: m	1·720	1·720
I: m^4	6·969	7·349
W_{sup}: m^3	6·570	6·931
W_{inf}: m^3	4·053	4·273
ρ	0·540	—

$$\rho = \frac{I}{A(h - y_c)y_c}$$

$\rho > 0·5$ (OK, good section efficiency according to Guyon[2])

For torsion

$$I_t = \frac{4A^2}{\oint (1/t)\,ds}$$

$$= \frac{2 \times 0·55 \times 0·20 \times (2·78 - 0·20)^2 \times (5·50 - 0·55)^2}{5·5 \times 0·55 + 2·78 \times 0·20 - 0·55^2 - 0·20^2} = 11·080 \text{ m}^4$$

Prestressing force (straight tendons only)

$$P_0 = (10 + 6) \times 1·456 = 23·296 \text{ MN}$$

Eccentricity of prestressing force

$$e = \frac{10 \times 2·592 + 6 \times 0·185}{16} - 1·720 = 1·689 - 1·720 = -0·031 \text{ m}$$

C4. Action effects during launching

(See also Zellner and Svensson.[3])

The action effects are calculated according to the theory of elasticity.

The cross-section considered in sections C6 and C7 is AA in Fig. C6.

Envelopes of maximum and minimum values of M_g are shown in Fig. C8.

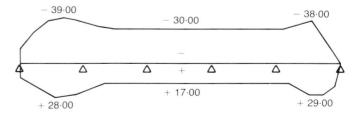

Fig. C8. Envelopes of maximum and minimum moments M_g (MN m) due to dead load

Fig. C9. Envelope of hyperstatic moments of prestressing, M_p (MN m)

Due to temperature difference of 2·5°C (sunshine)

$M = 2·30$ MN m (or $= 0$)

Due to settling of the supports (10 mm)

$M = 3·05$ MN m (or $= 0$)

Figs C9–C11 show envelopes of M_p, V_g and R_g.

. Time-pendent losses straight ndons

Prestressing force

3.3.3

$P = 10 \times 1·456 + 6 \times 1·456 =$

$14·560 + 8·736 = 23·296$ MN

At the levels of the straight tendons

$$W_{p\,sup} = \frac{7·349}{2·592 - 1·720} = 8·428 \text{ m}^3$$

$$W_{p\,inf} = \frac{7·349}{1·720 - 0·185} = 4·788 \text{ m}^3$$

Positive moment $M_g = 17·00$ MN m (M_p not taken into account)
Estimation of stresses

$$\sigma_{cg\,sup} = \frac{-17·00}{8·428} = -2·02 \text{ MN/m}^2$$

$$\sigma_{cg\,inf} = \frac{+17·00}{4·788} = +3·55 \text{ MN/m}^2$$

$$\sigma_{cp0\,sup} = \frac{-23·296}{7·352} - \frac{23·296 \times (-0·031)}{8·428} = -3·08 \text{ MN/m}^2$$

$$\sigma_{cp0\,inf} = \frac{-23·296}{7·352} + \frac{23·296 \times (-0·031)}{4·788} = -3·32 \text{ MN/m}^2$$

$(\sigma_{cg} + \sigma_{cp0})_{sup} = -5·10 \text{ MN/m}^2$

$(\sigma_{cg} + \sigma_{cp0})_{inf} = +0·23 \text{ MN/m}^2$

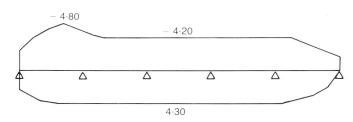

Fig. C10. Envelopes of maximum and minimum shear forces V_g (MN)
due to dead load

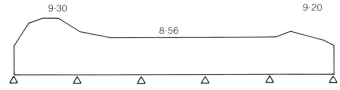

Fig. C11. Envelope of bearing reactions R_g (MN) due to dead load

Decompression ($\sigma_c = 0$) is slightly exceeded, but we use

$$\sigma_{pg0} = \sigma_{p0} = 1037 \text{ MN/m}^2 \qquad \textit{5.3.4}$$
$$\sigma_p = 1037 - 0.3\Delta\sigma_p$$

Top

$\Delta\sigma_p$ estimated 9%

$\Delta\sigma_p = 0.09 \times 1037 = 93.3 \text{ MN/m}^2$

$\sigma_p = 1037 - 0.3 \times 93.3 = 1009 \text{ MN/m}^2$

$\Delta\sigma_{pr} = -0.04 \times 1009 = -40.4 \text{ MN/m}^2$

$$\Delta\sigma_p = \frac{-0.22 \times 0.55 \times 205 - 40.4 + 5.7 \times 2.1 \times 0.55 \times (-5.10)}{1 + 5.7 \times (3.08/1037) \times (1 + 2.1 \times 0.55/2)} \qquad \textit{3.3.3}$$

$$= -96.2 \text{ MN/m}^2$$

corresponds to 9.3%   (OK)

Bottom

$\Delta\sigma_p$ estimated 6%

$\Delta\sigma_p = 0.06 \times 1037 = 62.2 \text{ MN/m}^2$

$\sigma_p = 1037 - 0.3 \times 62.2 = 1018 \text{ MN/m}^2$

$\Delta\sigma_{pr} = -0.04 \times 1018 = -40.7 \text{ MN/m}^2$

$$\Delta\sigma_p = \frac{-0.22 \times 0.55 \times 205 - 40.7 + 5.7 \times 2.1 \times 0.55 \times (+0.23)}{1 + 5.7 \times (3.32/1037) \times (1 + 2.1 \times 0.55/2)}$$

$$= -62.2 \text{ MN/m}^2$$

corresponds to 6.0%   (OK)

Negative moment $M_g = -30.00$ MN m ($M_p = 0$)
Estimation of stresses

$$\sigma_{cg \, sup} = \frac{-(-30.00)}{8.428} = +3.56 \text{ MN/m}^2$$

$$\sigma_{cg \, inf} = \frac{+(-30.00)}{4.788} = -6.27 \text{ MN/m}^2$$

$(\sigma_{cg} + \sigma_{cp0})_{sup} = +3.56 - 3.08 = +0.48 \text{ MN/m}^2$

$(\sigma_{cg} + \sigma_{cp0})_{inf} = -6.27 - 3.32 = -9.59 \text{ MN/m}^2$

Decompression is slightly exceeded, but we still use

$$\sigma_{pg0} = \sigma_{p0} = 1037 \text{ MN/m}^2$$

Top

$\Delta\sigma_p$ estimated 5.8%

$\Delta\sigma_p = 0.058 \times 1037 = 60.1 \text{ MN/m}^2$

$\Delta\sigma_{pr} = -0.04 \times (1037 - 0.3 \times 60.1) = -40.8 \text{ MN/m}^2$

$$\Delta\sigma_p = \frac{-24.81 - 40.8 + 5.7 \times 2.1 \times 0.55 \times 0.48}{1.030} = -60.6 \text{ MN/m}^2$$

corresponds to 5.8%   (OK)

Bottom

$\Delta\sigma_p$ estimated 11.8%

$\Delta\sigma_p = 0.118 \times 1037 = 122.4 \text{ MN/m}^2$

$$\Delta\sigma_{pr} = -0.04 \times (1037 - 0.3 \times 122.4) = -40.0 \text{ MN/m}^2$$

$$\Delta\sigma_p = \frac{-24.81 - 40.0 + 5.7 \times 2.1 \times 0.55 \times (-9.59)}{1.030}$$

$$= -124.4 \text{ MN/m}^2$$

corresponds to 12·0%   (OK)

Losses and forces

Due to these values the losses can be estimated.

Top

$$\frac{9.3 + 5.8}{2} = 7.6\%$$

Bottom

$$\frac{6.0 + 12.0}{2} = 9.0\%$$

It is quite safe to assume that, at the end of the launching period, the loss in the straight tendons is 10%.

$$t = 0.5 \text{ year}$$

$$P_{sup} = 0.9 \times 14.560 = 13.104 \text{ MN}$$

$$P_{inf} = 0.9 \times 8.736 = \underline{7.862 \text{ MN}}$$

$$\overline{20.966 \text{ MN}}$$

Serviceability ~~limi~~t state during ~~laun~~ching

C6.1. Bending moments in section AA

Because the actions were specified in agreement with the client, the values $\psi_1 = 1$ and $\psi_2 = 1$ were used.   *5.1.1*

$$\max M = 1.05 \times 17.00 + 2.00 + 3.05 + 2.30 = +25.20 \text{ MN m}$$

$$\min M = 1.05 \times (-30.00) = -31.50 \text{ MN m}$$

C6.2. Structure assumed uncracked

Maximum M

$$\sigma_{c\,sup} = -\frac{20.966}{7.352} - \frac{25.20 - 20.966 \times 0.031}{6.931} = -6.39 \text{ MN/m}^2$$

$$\sigma_{c\,inf} = -\frac{20.966}{7.352} + \frac{25.20 - 20.966 \times 0.031}{4.273} = +2.89 \text{ MN/m}^2$$

With max M the shear is about 0, so the principal diagonal tensile stress is $\approx \sigma_{c\,inf}$.

Top   *5.3.1*

$$\sigma_c < 0.5 f_{ck} = 20 \text{ MN/m}^2 \text{ (OK)}$$

Bottom   *5.3.2*

$$\sigma_c \approx \sigma_{ct} = 2.6 \text{ MN/m}^2 \text{ (OK (tolerated by client))}$$

($f_{ck} = 40$ MN/m², $h > 1000$ mm, good working conditions, high standard of control.)   *Fig. 5.2*

Minimum M

$$\sigma_{c\,sup} = -\frac{20.966}{7.352} - \frac{-31.50 - 20.966 \times 0.031}{6.931} = +1.79 \text{ MN/m}^2$$

$$\sigma_{c\,inf} = -\frac{20\cdot966}{7\cdot352} + \frac{-31\cdot50 - 20\cdot966 \times 0\cdot031}{4\cdot273} = -10\cdot38 \text{ MN/m}^2$$

(OK)

With min M

$$V = 4\cdot30 \text{ MN}$$

$$\tau_c = \frac{VS}{Ib_{ef}} = \frac{4\cdot30 \times 3\cdot211}{7\cdot349 \times 0\cdot90} = 2\cdot09 \text{ MN/m}^2$$

In the web

$$\sigma_c \leqslant +0\cdot50 \text{ MN/m}^2$$

Principal diagonal tensile stress (Guyon,[2] vol. 2, 41)

$$\sigma_{ct} = \frac{0\cdot50}{2} + \frac{1}{2}\sqrt{(0\cdot50^2 + 4 \times 2\cdot09^2)} = +2\cdot35 \text{ MN/m}^2$$

$$< 2\cdot60 \text{ MN/m}^2 \text{ (OK)}$$

C6.3. Structure assumed cracked[4]
See Fig. C12.

$$P = 20\cdot966 \text{ MN}$$

$$A_{s1} = 0\cdot0108 \text{ m}^2$$

$$A_{s2} = 0\cdot0214 \text{ m}^2$$

Both 16 mm dia. at 100 mm centres

$$c = 0\cdot050 \text{ m}$$

$$s = 0\cdot100 \text{ m}$$

max $M = +25\cdot20$ MN m

See Fig. C13.

$$\sigma_c = \frac{Px}{b_w x^2/2 + (b - b_w)(2x - h_f)h_f/2 - 15A_{s1}(d - x) - 15A_{s2}(d' - x)}$$

$$\sigma_c = \frac{-20\cdot966 \times 1\cdot14}{1\cdot10 \times 1\cdot14^2/2 + 4\cdot75 \times (2 \times 1\cdot14 - 0\cdot35) \times 0\cdot35 + 0\cdot0923}$$

$$= -5\cdot95 \text{ MN/m}^2$$

A_{s1}

$$\sigma_s = 15 \times 5\cdot95 \times \frac{2\cdot73 - 1\cdot14}{1\cdot14} = 124\cdot52 \text{ MN/m}^2 \qquad \text{(OK)}$$

The value used here for α is 15. For short term loading the value is 5·7. As there are both short and long term loadings, a value such as $\alpha = 10$ could also be justified.

min $M = -31\cdot50$ MN m

See Fig. C14.

$$\sigma_c = \frac{-20\cdot966 \times 2\cdot00}{1\cdot10 \times 2\cdot00^2/2 + 1\cdot85 \times (2 \times 2\cdot00 - 0\cdot30) \times 0\cdot30 + 0\cdot0816}$$

$$= -9\cdot67 \text{ MN/m}^2$$

A_{s2}

$$\sigma_s = 15 \times 9\cdot67 \times \frac{2\cdot73 - 2\cdot00}{2\cdot00} = 52\cdot96 \text{ MN/m}^2 \qquad \text{(OK)}$$

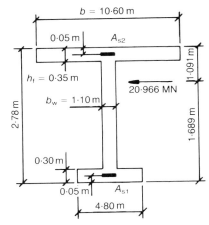

Fig. C12. Position of prestressing resultant

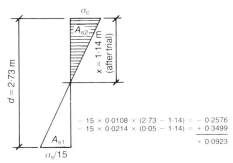

Fig. C13. Stresses under P + max. M (serviceability limit state)

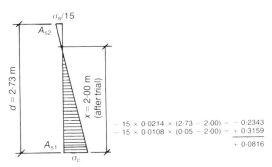

Fig. C14. Stresses under P + min. M (serviceability limit state)

Crack control
max $M = +25 \cdot 20$ MN m

$$M_r = 4 \cdot 273 \times \left\{ \frac{1}{7 \cdot 352} + \frac{0 \cdot 031}{4 \cdot 273} \right\} \times 20 \cdot 966 = 12 \cdot 84 \text{ MN m}$$

Here the cracking moment is equal to the decompression moment $(\sigma_c = 0)$ (safe side).

$$w_k = 0 \cdot 1 \times \left(1 \cdot 5 + \frac{3 \cdot 5 \times 0 \cdot 05}{0 \cdot 100} \right) \times \frac{124 \cdot 52}{2 \times 10^5} \times \left(1 - \left\{ \frac{12 \cdot 84}{25 \cdot 20} \right\}^2 \right) \times 10^3 \qquad 5.5.4$$

$$= 0 \cdot 150 \text{ mm} \qquad (OK)$$

min $M = -31 \cdot 50$ MN m

$$M_r = -6 \cdot 931 \times \left\{ \frac{1}{7 \cdot 352} - \frac{0 \cdot 031}{6 \cdot 931} \right\} \times 20 \cdot 966 = -19 \cdot 12 \text{ MN m}$$

$$w_k = 0.1 \times \left(1.5 + \frac{3.5 \times 0.05}{0.100}\right) \times \frac{52.96}{2 \times 10^5} \times \left(1 - \left\{\frac{19.12}{31.50}\right\}^2\right) \times 10^3$$

$$= 0.054 \text{ mm} \qquad \text{(OK)}$$

C7. Ultimate limit state

C7.1. Bending
max M

$$M_{Sd} = 1.35 \times (1.05 \times 17.00 + 2.00 + 3.05 + 2.30) = +34.02 \text{ MN m}$$

4.3

4.1.2

All the indirect action effects are taken with their full value (without ψ_0).

$$\sigma_c = 0.8 \times \frac{40}{1.5} = 21.3 \text{ MN/m}^2$$

See Fig. C15.

Tensile strain in the tendons caused by prestressing (after losses)

$$\varepsilon_{pt} = \frac{20.966}{16 \times 0.001\,404 \times 205 \times 10^3} = 0.00455$$

After trial

$$x = 0.166 \text{ m}$$

$$\varepsilon_c = 0.00060$$

Strain in the steels

$$A_{s1}: \qquad \varepsilon_{s1} = 0.01000$$

$$A_{p\,inf}: \quad \varepsilon_{p\,inf} = 0.00948 + 0.00455$$

$$A_{p\,sup}: \quad \varepsilon_{p\,sup} = 0.00009 + 0.00455$$

$$A_{s2}: \qquad \varepsilon_{s2} = -0.00045$$

Corresponding stress (including $\gamma_s = 1.15$)

$$A_{s1}: \qquad \sigma_{s1} = 348.0 \text{ MN/m}^2$$

$$A_{p\,inf}: \quad \sigma_{p\,inf} = 1061.0 \text{ MN/m}^2$$

$$A_{p\,sup}: \quad \sigma_{p\,sup} = 951.2 \text{ MN/m}^2$$

$$A_{s2}: \qquad \sigma_{s2} = -92.5 \text{ MN/m}^2$$

Duct holes must be subtracted from the compressive zone. The prestressing force in this zone has been taken into account with coefficient 1·35 for the permanent loads.

Duct holes in the deck slab

$$A_\phi = 10\pi \times 0.075^2/4 = 0.0442 \text{ m}^2$$

$$F_c = 21.3 \times (10.5 \times 0.8 \times 0.166 - 0.0442)$$

$$+92.5 \times 0.0214 - 1.35 \times 10 \times 951.2 \times 0.001404$$

$$= 12.710 \text{ MN} \quad (y = 2.714 \text{ m})$$

$$F_s = 6 \times 1061.0 \times 0.001404 + 348.0 \times 0.0108$$

$$= 12.696 \text{ MN} \quad (y = 0.145 \text{ m})$$

With sufficient accuracy

$$F_c = F_s$$

Thus, in the direction of positive moment, the bending capacity is

$$M_{Rd} = 12.696 \times (2.714 - 0.145) = 32.617 \text{ MN m}$$

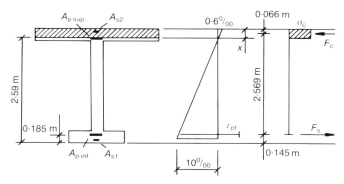

Fig. C15. Strains and internal forces at ultimate limit state, for max. M

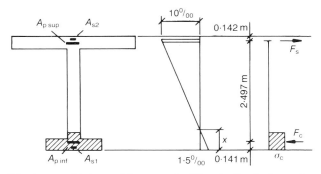

Fig. C16. Strains and internal forces at ultimate limit state, for min. M

Because $M_{Rd} < M_{Sd}$, the steel area in the tensile side has to be slightly increased.

Here we take into account the upper layer of reinforcement in the bottom slab: $0 \cdot 0042$ m^2/$0 \cdot 130$ m (12 mm dia., 100 mm centres).

Repeating the same calculation gives

$$F_s = 12 \cdot 696 + 0 \cdot 0042 \times 348 = 14 \cdot 158 \text{ MN} \qquad (y = 0 \cdot 143 \text{ m})$$

$$F_c = 13 \cdot 835 \text{ MN} \qquad (y = 2 \cdot 712 \text{ m})$$

$$M_{Rd} = 13 \cdot 835 \times (2 \cdot 712 - 0 \cdot 143) = 35 \cdot 542 \text{ MN m}$$

which is sufficient (OK).

min M

$$M_{Sd} = -1 \cdot 35 \times 31 \cdot 50 = -42 \cdot 53 \text{ MN m}$$

The indirect action effects are >0 or $=0$.

See Fig. C16.

After trial

$$x = 0 \cdot 352 \text{ m}$$

$$\varepsilon_c = 0 \cdot 00150$$

See Table C2.

Duct holes in bottom slab

$$A_\phi = 6 \times \pi \times (0 \cdot 075/2)^2 = 0 \cdot 0265 \text{ m}^2$$

$$F_c = 21 \cdot 3 \times (4 \cdot 8 \times 0 \cdot 8 \times 0 \cdot 352 - 0 \cdot 0265)$$

$$+ 260 \cdot 3 \times 0 \cdot 0108 - 1 \cdot 35 \times 6 \times 789 \cdot 4 \times 0 \cdot 001404$$

$$= 22 \cdot 060 \text{ MN} \qquad (y = 0 \cdot 141 \text{ m})$$

$$F_s = 10 \times 1061 \cdot 0 \times 0 \cdot 001404 + 348 \cdot 0 \times 0 \cdot 0214$$
$$= 22 \cdot 344 \text{ MN} \qquad (y = 2 \cdot 638 \text{ m})$$
$$M_{Rd} = -22 \cdot 060 \times (2 \cdot 638 - 0 \cdot 141) = -55 \cdot 84 \text{ MN m}$$
$$|M_{Rd}| > |M_{Sd}| \qquad \text{(OK)}$$

C7.2. Shear

4.4
Straight tendons only: $\alpha_p = 0°$

4.4.2
Stirrups: $\alpha = 90°$

V from Fig. C10.

$$f_{ck} = 40 \text{ MN/m}^2$$ *Tab*

$$\tau_{Rd} = 0 \cdot 42 \text{ MN/m}^2$$

$$V_{Sd} = \gamma_g V = 1 \cdot 35 \times 4 \cdot 30 = 5 \cdot 81 \text{ MN}$$ *Tab*

There are in the webs still four empty ducts for the curved tendons (Figs C5 and C6).

$$b_{w \text{ nom}} = 2 \times 0 \cdot 50 - 0 \cdot 5 \times (4 \times 0 \cdot 075) = 0 \cdot 850 \text{ m}$$

$$V_{Rd2} = 0 \cdot 3 f_{cd} \, b_w \, d = 0 \cdot 30 \times 26 \cdot 7 \times 0 \cdot 85 \times 2 \cdot 73 = 18 \cdot 59 \text{ MN}$$

$$5 \cdot 81 \text{ MN} < 18 \cdot 59 \text{ MN} \qquad \text{(OK)}$$ *4.4.2*

$M_{Sdu} = -42 \cdot 53 \text{ MN m (as in bending)}$

$M_0 = M_r = -19 \cdot 12 \text{ MN m (no partial safety coefficient is applied)}.$

Effect of tolerances on V_{Sd}

See Fig. C17.

$$\varphi = \frac{7}{2700} = 0 \cdot 0026$$

No partial safety coefficient is applied to the effect of torsion due to geometric imperfections because the quantity 7 mm itself is contractual.

Corresponding torsion, bearing reaction and shear force

$$T_{Sd} = \frac{\varphi G I_t}{l} = \frac{0 \cdot 0026 \times 15\,000 \times 11 \cdot 080}{45} = 9 \cdot 60 \text{ MN m}$$

$$\Delta R = \frac{9 \cdot 60}{4 \cdot 16} = 2 \cdot 31 \text{ MN} \qquad (+/-)$$

$$\Delta V_{Sd} = 0 \cdot 5 \times 2 \cdot 31 = 1 \cdot 15 \text{ MN}$$

In one web

$$V_{Sd} = 0 \cdot 5 \times 5 \cdot 81 + 1 \cdot 15 = 4 \cdot 05 \text{ MN}$$

$$b_{w \text{ nom}} = 0 \cdot 5 \times 0 \cdot 85 = 0 \cdot 425 \text{ m}$$

Table C2. Steel strains and stresses at ultimate limit state

	ε	σ: MN/m^2
A_{s1}	$-0 \cdot 00109$	$-260 \cdot 3$
$A_{p \text{ inf}}$	$-0 \cdot 00070 + 0 \cdot 00455$	$789 \cdot 4$
$A_{p \text{ sup}}$	$0 \cdot 00942 + 0 \cdot 00455$	$1061 \cdot 0$
A_{s2}	$0 \cdot 01000$	$348 \cdot 0$

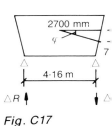

Fig. C17

$$V_{cd} = 2 \cdot 5 \times 0 \cdot 42 \times 0 \cdot 425 \times 2 \cdot 73 \times \left(1 + \frac{19 \cdot 12}{42 \cdot 53}\right) = 1 \cdot 77 \text{ MN}$$ 4.4.2(b)

$$V_{wd} = 4 \cdot 05 - 1 \cdot 77 = 2 \cdot 28 \text{ MN}$$

$$A_{sw} = \frac{2 \cdot 28}{0 \cdot 9 \times 2 \cdot 73 \times 348} = 0 \cdot 00267 \text{ m}^2/\text{m} = 2670 \text{ mm}^2/\text{m}$$

Two dia. 16 mm at 150 mm centres: approx. 2680 mm^2/m (OK).

$$\rho_w = \frac{2 \times 2 \cdot 01 \times 10^{-4} \times 10^2}{0 \cdot 15 \times 0 \cdot 425} = 0 \cdot 63\%$$ 4.4.2(c)

$$0 \cdot 63\% > 0 \cdot 15\% \quad \text{(OK)}$$

The tolerances lead also to a greater bending moment and shear concentration in the other web and this must be taken into consideration in serviceability limit state calculations (stresses and crack widths).

In the ultimate limit state the yielding signifies such great deformations (in ductile structures) that the bending moments can be regarded as equal in two webs. This is not the case for shear because shear rupture is not a ductile rupture.

C7.3. Combined torsion, shear and bending 4.5
4.5.1

The torsional resistance is not strictly speaking necessary for the equilibrium of the bridge, but it is very beneficial for live load distribution. Thus one does not want the bridge to be badly cracked in launching.

The following values are chosen 4.5.2

$h_{ef} = 0 \cdot 20$ m (thickness of bottom slab)

$\theta = 45°$

$A_{ef} = 14 \cdot 7$ m^2

Then

$$T_{Rd} = 0 \cdot 50 \times 26 \cdot 7 \times 14 \cdot 7 \times 0 \cdot 20 \sin(2 \times 45°)$$
$$= 39 \cdot 25 \text{ MN m}$$

$$\frac{V_{Sd}}{V_{Rd}} = \frac{5 \cdot 81 + 2 \cdot 30}{18 \cdot 59} = \frac{8 \cdot 11}{18 \cdot 59} = 0 \cdot 44$$

$$\frac{T_{Sd}}{T_{Rd}} = \frac{9 \cdot 60}{39 \cdot 25} = 0 \cdot 24$$

$$\frac{T_{Sd}}{T_{Rd}} + \frac{V_{Sd}}{V_{Rd}} = 0 \cdot 24 + 0 \cdot 44 = 0 \cdot 68$$

$$0 \cdot 68 < 1 \quad \text{(OK)}$$

Torsional reinforcement 4.5.2(c)

(a) Stirrups

$$\frac{A_s}{s} = \frac{T_{Sd}}{2 A_{ef} f_{ywd}} \tan \theta = \frac{9 \cdot 60 \times 1 \cdot 0 \times 10^6}{2 \times 14 \cdot 7 \times 348} = 940 \text{ mm}^2/\text{m}$$

(b) Longitudinal

$$\frac{A_l}{u_{ef}} = \frac{T_{Sd}}{2 A_{ef} f_{yld}} \cot \theta = \frac{9 \cdot 60 \times 1 \cdot 0 \times 10^6}{2 \times 14 \cdot 7 \times 348} = 940 \text{ mm}^2/\text{m}$$

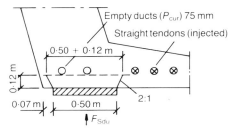

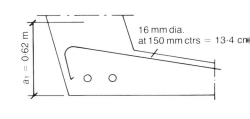

Fig. C18   *Fig. C19*

C7.4. Local force effects
Reaction over the sliding bearings

Three rubber bearings 0.50 m by 0.35 m in succession under one web (see Fig. C18).

$$A_{c0} = 3 \times 0.50 \times 0.35 = 0.525 \text{ m}^2$$

From Fig. C11

$$R = 8.56 \text{ MN}$$

From section C7.2

$$\Delta R = 2.31 \text{ MN}$$

$$\max F_{Sdu} = 1.35 \times (0.5 \times 8.56 + 2.31) = 8.90 \text{ MN} \qquad\qquad 6.4.1$$

The enlargement level is chosen according to the lowest position of the curved tendons. The empty ducts are subtracted.

$$A_{c1} = (0.50 + 0.12 - 2 \times 0.075) \times (3 \times 0.35 + 0.12) = 0.550 \text{ m}^2$$

$$F_{Rdu} = 26.7\sqrt{(0.550 \times 0.525)} = 14.35 \text{ MN}$$

Therefore

$$\max F_{Sdu} < F_{Rdu} \qquad \text{(OK)}$$

Also

$$F_{Rdu} \ll 3.3 \times 26.7 \times 0.525 = 46.26 \text{ MN} \qquad \text{(OK)}$$

Transverse tensile force

$$F_{Std} = 0.3 \times 8.90 \times \left\{ 1 - \frac{0.50}{0.62} \right\} = 0.517 \text{ MN}$$

$$A_s = \frac{0.517}{0.0348} = 14.8 \text{ cm}^2; \qquad \frac{14.8}{1.17} = 12.7 \text{ cm}^2/\text{m}$$

$$a_1 = 0.50 + 0.12 = 0.62 \text{ m} \qquad\qquad\qquad\qquad Fig. 6$$

See Fig. C19.

References

1. Garrett A. J. and Templeman R. B. Incrementally launched concrete bridges. *Proc. Sino-British Highways and Urban Traffic Conference, Beijing, 1986.* Institution of Highways and Transportation, London.
2. Guyon Y. *Constructions en béton précontraint.* Eyrolles, Paris, 1968.
3. Zellner W. and Svensson H. Incremental launching of structures. *J. Struct. Engng Div. Am. Soc. Civ. Engrs,* 1983, **109**, Feb., No. 2.
4. Thonier H. Le projet de béton armé. *Annls Inst. Tech. Bâtim.,* 1986, June–Nov.

Example D   Nadachigawa Bridge, Niigata, Japan: three-span box girder bridge for Hokuriku Expressway

Balanced cantilever method

Example prepared by H. Nakayama (Tokyo), with the assistance of H. R. Ganz (Berne), S. Pérez-Fadón (Madrid) and J. Shimoni (Tel Aviv)

References to *FIP recommendations: Practical design of reinforced and prestressed concrete structures (based on the CEB–FIP model code (MC78))* are given in the right-hand margin

1. Cantilever Construction

Cantilever construction, which is very widely used for long-span bridges, is carried out in individual cast in situ or precast segments, beginning either at the abutments or at intermediate piers. In the latter case, the superstructure is built out simultaneously from both sides as symmetrically as possible to give a balanced cantilever construction.

The main design criterion for this simple and well tried construction method is the proper dimensioning of the longitudinal prestressing. This must be chosen such that

(a) vertical displacements of the large cantilevers during construction remain small and stay within the anticipated longitudinal profile
(b) the long term deformations due to creep and shrinkage of the finished structure do not exceed acceptable limits
(c) the safety of the structure is guaranteed at all stages.

The first two criteria require very elaborate calculations for serviceability limit state, in which all long term effects (creep, shrinkage, relaxation, temperature, etc.) are taken into account for all successive construction stages and for the completed structure. These calculations are not presented here, as they are beyond the scope of this handbook. However, it is evident that the unfavourable consequences of these effects can be greatly reduced or even offset by the choice of a higher degree of prestressing than is strictly statically necessary. For example, in the case of full load-balancing (i.e. if at each stage the moments of prestress have the same magnitude as the cantilever moments but the opposite sign), the sections are subjected to axial compression only, and no angular or vertical deformation will result. This method of full load-balancing is rather expensive and may lead to too great a margin of safety. Nevertheless, in view of the fact that a great number of cantilever bridges developed undesirable deflections and some of them had to be repaired at high cost, it is certainly advisable to dimension the longitudinal prestress rather amply, in particular for the first segments, which contribute most to potentially detrimental deformation.

As far as the third criterion is concerned, the application of the theory of plasticity is certainly most appropriate (e.g. in the ultimate limit state check). The thorny question of the moment redistribution after closure of the central gap does not arise in such a calculation.

Prestressing tendons can be either round bars, or cables of different numbers of wires or strands, placed in sheathed ducts. Bars have the advantage that they can easily be coupled in an alternating pattern. They are anchored in the joints between segments according to the shape of the moment diagram for a cantilever beam.

Each formwork traveller can be moved forward to the end of the completed portion of the bridge, where it is cantilevered out to provide the formwork for the next segment to be constructed. It carries the weight of the new segment until the concrete is cured and the bars which ended there have been stressed and anchored. The prestress force to be provided in each segment is such that the new segment is tied into the previously completed portion of the bridge and can carry the weight of the traveller as well as the concrete of the next segment.

The prestressing force has to be distributed among a number of tendons in order that a sufficient number of them can be anchored at the end of each segment. Therefore in longer spans it is advisable to decrease the number of tendons by choosing cables rather than bars, with increased forces of up to 2000 kN per cable and more.

In this case study, ribbed sheaths are placed in the concrete cross-section to provide ducts for the prestressing cables that end in the following segments. Sheaths should be stiffened—for example, by the insertion of thin-walled steel tubes—so that they retain their exact position during concreting operations. The sheaths are coupled together in sections and the inserted tubes are pulled into the next segment to be concreted. The tubing guarantees an exactly curved and open duct, which allows even long prestressing cables to be threaded through the duct with ease after concreting.

The ability to thread through subsequently only those cables which end with the new segment has the added advantage that the cables lie exposed to corrosion in the structure for only a very short time. As soon as the newly concreted segment has been cured and prestressed, the duct can be injected with grout, thereby creating a bond between cable and concrete member.

Balanced cantilever construction from a pier requires men and materials to be transported to the pier sites, even if the piers are located in water or difficult terrain. After work has been completed at one pier site, the formwork travellers must be transferred to the next. This disadvantage is avoided if cantilever construction begins at the end of the bridge. But then the relatively long cantilevers that result before the next pier is reached have to be tied back by cable stays and temporary pylons. The pylons are relocated once the superstructure rests on the next pier. Work proceeds in only one direction (as in this example), or from both ends towards the middle.

For a continuous series of longer spans, segmental span-by-span construction which employs a launching gantry can be recommended. The gantry is rolled forward on the completed portion of the bridge to its next concreting position, where it is supported by the end of the bridge and the next pier. In this position, it extends a half-span beyond the pier. Beginning at the pier, construction proceeds symmetrically from both sides until the already completed portion is reached. The gantry is then rolled forward another span. This method allows the use of precast or cast-in-place segments. Site and construction conditions as well as the construction schedule determine which variation is preferable and the length of segment to be selected.

The launching gantry serves not only as a guideway for the travelling formwork but also as a bridge for the transport of men and materials between the completed portion of the bridge and the segments under construction above the next pier. A further variation of this construction method does not require the launching gantry to carry the weight of the concrete structure. The gantry serves only as a transport bridge for men and materials; other loads are assigned to the cantilevering concrete girder.

Whether long bridges are segmentally built in situ, or with precast elements, or by a combination of the two methods, and how large the individual segments are to be depends on the local conditions and the size of the bridge.

During construction, geometric control is essential. Particular attention during the erection phase must be given to the control of dead loads in comparison with the actual prestressing. This greatly influences the creep deformations. Especially in long-span structures, concrete shrinkage and temperature changes have a considerable effect on long term and short term deformations.

It is advisable to have sufficient reinforcement in the longitudinal direction, even with segmental construction. This can also be achieved with prefabricated elements, spare holes being provided in which reinforcement—prestressed or not prestressed—can be inserted and grouted. With no longitudinal reinforcement across the joints, a higher degree of prestressing is necessary, especially if unbonded external tendons are used.

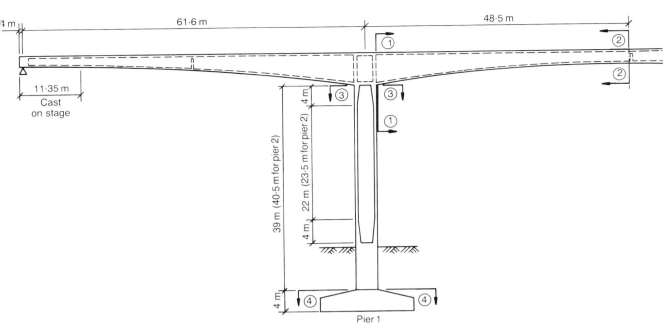

Fig. D1. Elevation

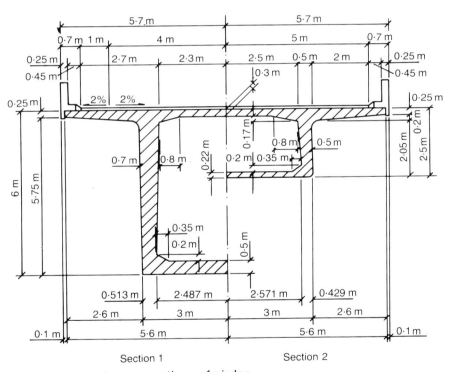

Fig. D2. Typical cross-sections of girder

A minimum amount of reinforcement should be provided and careful detailing applied, especially to distribute concentrated pre-stressing forces.

D2. Design information

D2.1. Structural summary
System (Fig. D1): rigid-frame continuous highway bridge, span lengths 61·6 m, 97·0 m and 61·6 m.

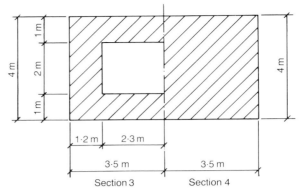

Fig. D3. Typical cross-sections of pier

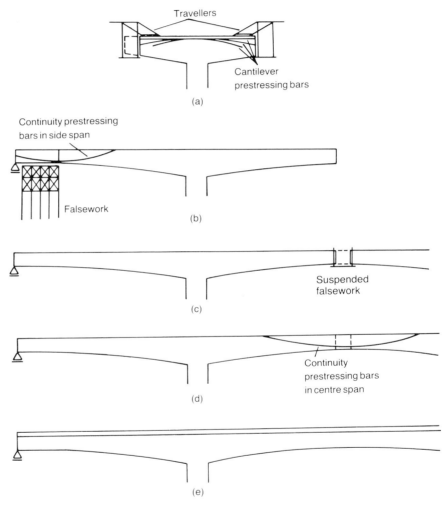

Fig. D4. Construction sequence: (a) balanced cantilever erection with travellers; (b) construction of side-span end section on falsework, and stressing of continuity prestressing bars in side span; (c) construction of centre-span closure section on suspended falsework; (d) stressing of continuity prestressing bars in centre span; (e) surfacing

Table D1. Criteria for checking tensile stresses in concrete

	During construction	After completion	
Superstructure	σ_{ct} (extreme fibre) $\leqslant 0.5$ MN/m^2	Fully prestressed	*3.4.3*
Substructure	Crack width $w \leqslant 0.1$ mm	$w \leqslant 0.1$ mm	*5.5.3*

Cross-section (Figs D2 and D3): superstructure—prestressed concrete one-cell box girder; substructure—reinforced concrete rectangular hollow pier.

Construction method: cast in place balanced cantilever method (Fig. D4).

D2.2. Materials
Concrete

   pier   C35

   girder   C40

Reinforcing steel S400

Prestressing steel (bars)

  S800/1050

  dia. 32 mm

  $A_p = 7 \cdot 89 \text{ cm}^2$

D2.3. Loading conditions
Dead load
Self-weight 25 kN/m³   *2.1.6*
Surfacing 38 kN/m

Prestressing force (including immediate losses)
Considering the allowable tensile stresses in the prestressing steel at the moment of tensioning and after transfer, and the immediate losses, the average prestressing forces are estimated as follows

   cantilever prestressing bars $P_1 = 470 \text{ kN}$

   continuity prestressing bars in side span $P_2 = 465 \text{ kN}$

   continuity prestressing bars in centre span $P_3 = 440 \text{ kN}$

Live load
According to Appendix 1 of the FIP recommendations (type H1, heavy).

Effect of temperature change
Whole structure $\pm 10°$C.
   The temperature gradient in the girder is not considered here in order to simplify this design example.

Earthquake
Horizontal seismic coefficients

   0·17 (after completion)

   0·085 (during construction)

The seismic coefficients are determined as the ratios of equivalent static forces to self-weight, considering the earthquake activities at the site, the seismic response related to the natural period of the structure, etc.

Wind
Wind loads are not considered, because they are not critical in this example (covered by earthquake).

D2.4. Serviceability conditions
The compressive stresses in the concrete are checked under infre-   *5.3.1*
quent combinations of actions; the tensile stresses are checked under frequent combinations, based on the criteria in Table D1.

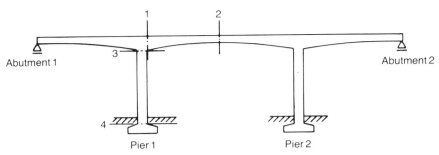

Fig. D5. Notation

D2.5. Sections checked in the example
In this example, only the four sections shown in Fig. D5 are checked.

D3. Basic data

D3.1. Concrete
See Table D2.

Creep and shrinkage according to Appendix e of the CEB–FIP model code (MC78) (relative humidity 70%).

D3.2. Reinforcing steel
High bond.

Strength: $f_{yk} = 400$ MN/m^2.

E-modulus: $E_s = 200\,000$ MN/m^2.

D3.3. Prestressing steel

Characteristic strength: $f_{0 \cdot 1k} = 800$ MN/m^2.

Tensile strength: $f_{tk} = 1050$ MN/m^2.

E-modulus: $E_s = 200\,000$ MN/m^2.

Relaxation 3%.

The relaxation value of 3% for prestressing bars is given in the Japanese *Specifications for highway bridges.*[1]

2.1

2.2

2.3

D4. Acting forces and moments

The acting forces and moments are obtained by elastic two-dimensional frame analysis taking into account the construction procedure.

The effects of creep and shrinkage are estimated by step-by-step calculation.

The moments caused by main actions after completion are shown in Figs D6–D13.

(a) *Variable actions.* The variable actions have maximum and minimum forces and moments, but only the values critical in the

Table D2. Concrete data

	C40	C35
Compressive strength, f_{ck}: MN/m^2	40	35
Tensile strength, f_{ctm}: MN/m^2	3·3	3·1
E-modulus, E_{cm}: MN/m^2	35 000	33 500

Fig. 2
Fig. 2

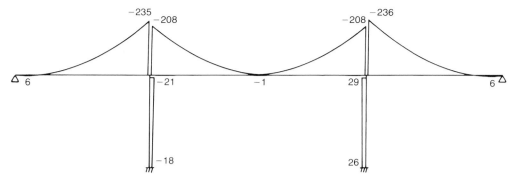

Fig. D6. Bending moments (MN m)—self-weight

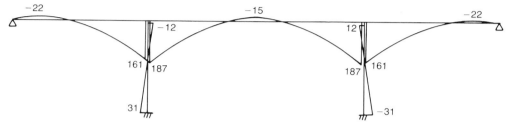

Fig. D7. Bending moments (MN m)—prestress

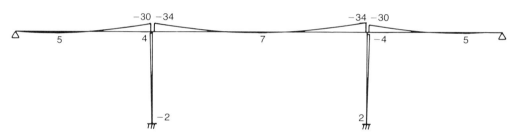

Fig. D8. Bending moments (MN m)—surfacing

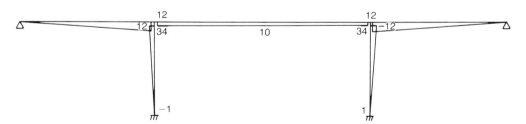

Fig. D9. Bending moments (MN m)—redistribution due to creep

combinations are shown. The values of the bending moment and the axial force for an action occur simultaneously at the critical condition for bending, and the value of the shear force occurs at the critical condition for shear.

(b) *Time-dependent changes.* The redistributions due to creep, shrinkage and prestress loss are time-dependent changes: the states before the changes, after partial changes and after complete changes must be considered. In this example, the state after the changes are complete is critical, and the values for time → ∞ are shown.

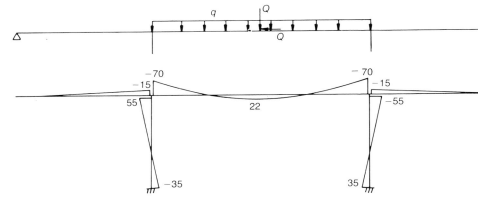

Fig. D10. Bending moments (MN m)—live load case 1: distributed load, q = 75 kN/m; concentrated load and longitudinal load, Q = 400 kN

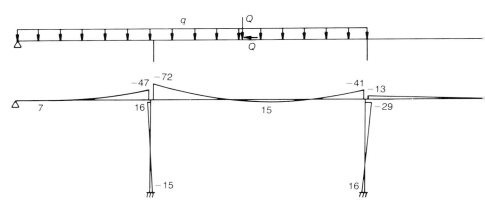

Fig. D11. Bending moments (MN m)—live load case 2: distributed load, q = 60 kN/m; concentrated load and longitudinal load, Q = 400 kN

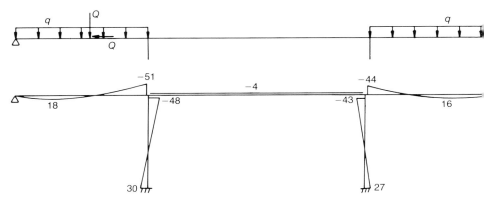

Fig. D12. Bending moments (MN m)—live load case 3: distributed load, q = 81 kN/m; concentrated load and longitudinal load, Q = 400 kN

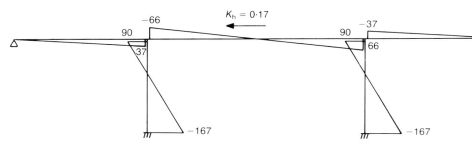

Fig. D13. Bending moments (MN m)—earthquake

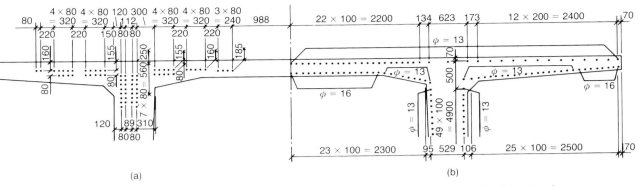

(a)

(b)

Fig. D14. Arrangement of prestressing and reinforcing steel in tension zone, section 1 (dimensions in millimetres): (a) prestressing bars; (b) reinforcing bars

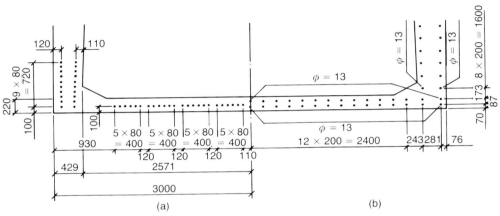

(a)

(b)

Fig. D15. Arrangement of prestressing and reinforcing steel in tension zone, section 2 (dimensions in millimetres): (a) prestressing bars; (b) reinforcing bars

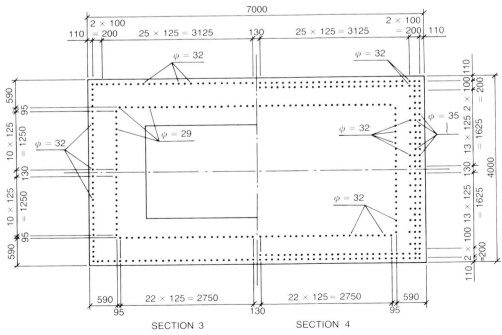

SECTION 3   SECTION 4

Fig. D16. Arrangement of reinforcement, sections 3 and 4 (dimensions in millimetres)

Table D3. Section properties

	Section 1	Section 2	Section 3	Secti‹
Section area, A: m^2	13·165	7·017	18·800	28·(
Centroid from top, y_o: m	2·715	0·898	2·000	2·(
Centroid from bottom, y_u: m	3·285	1·602	2·000	2·(
Moment of inertia, I: m^4	66·820	5·940	34·267	37·:

Table D4. Stages checked in this example

Section	Stages checked
1	After construction of segment 1* After construction of segment 25†
2	After construction of segment 27 (closure)
3	After construction of segment 25
4	After construction of segment 25

* Check for $M > 0$ under low axial force level.
† Check for $M < 0$ under high axial force level.

Table D5. Acting forces and moments at serviceability limit state: section 1 du‹
ing construction (after construction of segment 1)

Action	Bending moment: MN m	Axial force: MN	Shear forc‹ MN
Self-weight, G_0	−1·38	0·00	0·66
Prestress, P	4·41	−1·88	0·00
Traveller weight, G_w	0·00	0·00	0·00
Temperature change, T	0·00	0·00	0·00
Earthquake, E	0·00	−0·06	0·00
Frequent combination $G_0 + P + G_w + 0.5T$	3·03	−1·88	0·66
Infrequent combination $G_0 + P + G_w + T + 0.5E$ $G_0 + P + G_w + E + 0.5T$	3·03 3·03	−1·91 −1·94	0·66 0·66

Table D6. Acting forces and moments at serviceability limit state: section
during construction (after construction of segment 25)

Action	Bending moment: MN m	Axial force: MN	Shear forc‹ MN
Self-weight, G_0	−196·34	0·00	9·71
Prestress, P	167·53	−71·45	0·00
Traveller weight, G_w	−36·84	0·00	0·85
Temperature change, T	0·00	0·00	0·00
Earthquake, E	0·00	0·90	0·00
Frequent combination $G_0 + P + G_w + 0.5T$	−65·65	−71·45	10·56
Infrequent combination $G_0 + P + G_w + T + 0.5E$ $G_0 + P + G_w + E + 0.5T$	−65·65 −65·65	−71·90 −72·35	10·56 10·56

Serviceability t state

D5.1. Sections

Stress conditions, not only after completion but also during construction, are checked at sections 1–4 in this example. The section properties are given in Table D3. Prestressing and reinforcing steel is shown in Figs D14–D16.

D5.2. During construction

D5.2.1. Stages

Table D4 shows the stages at which sections 1–4 are checked in this example. The segments are shown in Fig. D17.

Table D7. Acting forces and moments at serviceability limit state: section 2 during construction (after construction of segment 27)

Action	Bending moment: MN m	Axial force: MN	Shear force: MN
Self-weight, G_0	−0·81	0·08	0·14
Prestress, P	−15·80	−34·10	0·00
Temperature change, T	−1·08	−0·32	0·00
Earthquake, E	−1·09	0·15	−0·70
Frequent combination $G_0 + P + 0·5T$	−17·15	−34·19	0·14
Infrequent combination $G_0 + P + T + 0·5E$	−18·24	−34·28	−0·21
$G_0 + P + E + 0·5T$	−18·24	−34·04	−0·56

Table D8. Acting forces and moments at serviceability limit state: section 3 during construction (after construction of segment 25)

Action	Bending moment: MN m	Axial force: MN	Shear force: MN
Self-weight, G_0	−25·90	−21·24	0·00
Traveller weight, G_w	−44·92	−0·85	0·00
Temperature change, T	0·00	0·00	0·00
Earthquake, E	−5·94	0·00	−1·81
Frequent combination $G_0 + G_w + 0·5T$	−70·82	−22·09	0·00
Infrequent combination $G_0 + G_w + T + 0·5E$	−73·79	−22·09	−0·91
$G_0 + G_w + E + 0·5T$	−76·76	−22·09	−1·81

Table D9. Acting forces and moments at serviceability limit state: section 4 during construction (after construction of segment 25)

Action	Bending moment: MN m	Axial force: MN	Shear force: MN
Self-weight, G_0	−25·90	−38·14	0·00
Traveller weight, G_w	−44·92	−0·85	0·00
Temperature change, T	0·00	0·00	0·00
Earthquake, E	−99·57	0·00	−3·11
Frequent combination $G_0 + G_w + 0·5T$	−70·82	−38·99	0·00
Infrequent combination $G_0 + G_w + T + 0·5E$	−120·61	−38·99	−1·56
$G_0 + G_w + E + 0·5T$	−170·39	−38·99	−3·11

The values of the acting forces and moments are shown in Tables D5–D9.

D5.2.2. Compressive stresses in concrete   5.3.*
Infrequent combination of actions.

Section 1 (after construction of segment 1)
Bending moment and axial force under infrequent combination

$$M = 3{\cdot}03 \text{ MN m}$$

$$N = -1{\cdot}94 \text{ MN}$$

Concrete stress at top fibre

$$\sigma_c = \frac{N}{A} - \frac{M}{I} y_0$$

$$= \frac{-1{\cdot}94}{13{\cdot}165} - \frac{3{\cdot}03}{66{\cdot}82} \times 2{\cdot}715 = -0{\cdot}27 \text{ MN/m}^2$$

$$|\sigma_c| < 0{\cdot}5 f_{ck} = 20 \text{ MN/m}^2$$

Section 1 (after construction of segment 25)

$$M = -65{\cdot}65 \text{ MN m}$$

$$N = -72{\cdot}35 \text{ MN}$$

Concrete stress at bottom fibre

$$\sigma_c = -8{\cdot}72 \text{ MN/m}^2$$

$$|\sigma_c| < 0{\cdot}5 f_{ck} = 20 \text{ MN/m}^2$$

Section 2 (after construction of segment 27)

$$M = -18{\cdot}24 \text{ MN m}$$

$$N = -34{\cdot}28 \text{ MN}$$

Concrete stress at bottom fibre

$$\sigma_c = -9{\cdot}80 \text{ MN/m}^2$$

$$|\sigma_c| < 0{\cdot}5 f_{ck} = 20 \text{ MN/m}^2$$

Section 3 (after construction of segment 25)

$$M = -76{\cdot}76 \text{ MN m}$$

$$N = -22{\cdot}09 \text{ MN}$$

Tensile stress as an uncracked section

$$\sigma_{ct} = \frac{-22{\cdot}09}{18{\cdot}8} - \frac{-76{\cdot}76}{34{\cdot}267} \times 2{\cdot}0$$

$$= 3{\cdot}31 \text{ MN/m}^2 > 0{\cdot}7 f_{ctm} = 2{\cdot}17 \text{ MN/m}^2$$

Therefore the section is considered cracked, and from the calculation for a cracked section (Fig. D16)

$$\sigma_c = -8{\cdot}6 \text{ MN/m}^2$$

$$|\sigma_c| < 0{\cdot}5 f_{ck} = 17{\cdot}5 \text{ MN/m}^2$$

See Fig. D18.

Section 4 (after construction of segment 25)

$$M = -170{\cdot}39 \text{ MN m}$$

$$N = -38{\cdot}99 \text{ MN}$$

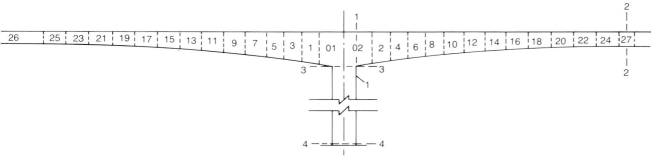

Fig. D17. Numbering of segments

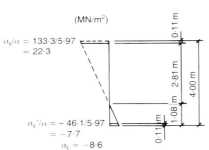

Fig. D18. Section 3: stresses at SLS (infrequent combination during construction)

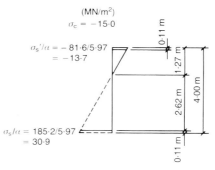

Fig. D19. Section 4: stresses at SLS (infrequent combination during construction)

$$\sigma_{ct} = 7.74 \text{ MN/m}^2 > 0.7 f_{ctm} = 2.17 \text{ MN/m}^2$$

Therefore the section is considered cracked, and from the calculation for a cracked section (Fig. D16)

$$\sigma_c = -15.0 \text{ MN/m}^2$$

$$|\sigma_c| < 0.5 f_{ck} = 17.5 \text{ MN/m}^2$$

See Fig. D19.

D5.2.3. Tensile stresses in concrete
Infrequent combination of actions.

3.4.3(b)

Section 1 (after construction of segment 1)
Bending moment and axial force under frequent combination

$$M = 3.03 \text{ MN m}$$

$$N = -1.88 \text{ MN}$$

$$V = 0.66 \text{ MN}$$

Concrete stress at bottom fibre

$$\sigma_{ct} = \frac{N}{A} + \frac{M}{I} y_u$$

$$= \frac{-1.88}{13.165} + \frac{3.03}{66.820} \times 3.285$$

$$= 0.01 \text{ MN/m}^2 \text{ (tension)} > 0$$

Limit of concrete tensile stress

$$\sigma_{ct \, lim} = 0.75 f_{ctk}$$

$$= 0.75 \times 0.7 f_{ctm}$$

2.1.3
Fig. 2.2
3.4.3

$$= 0.75 \times 0.7 \times 3.3$$
$$= 1.73 \text{ MN/m}^2 > 0.01 \text{ MN/m}^2$$

Section 1 (after construction of segment 25)

$$M = -65.65 \text{ MN m}$$
$$N = -71.45 \text{ MN}$$
$$V = 10.56 \text{ MN}$$

$$\sigma_{ct} = \frac{-71.45}{13.165} - \frac{-65.65}{66.820} \times 2.715$$

$$= -2.76 \text{ MN/m}^2 \text{ (compression)} < 0 \text{ MN/m}^2$$

Principal stress in web

$$\sigma_I = \frac{\sigma_x + \sigma_y}{2} + \frac{1}{2} \sqrt{[(\sigma_x - \sigma_y)^2 + 4\tau^2]}$$

At centroid

$$\sigma_x = \frac{N}{A} = \frac{-71.45}{13.165} = -5.43 \text{ MN/m}^2$$

$$\sigma_y = 0$$

$$\tau = \frac{V_s S}{b_w I}$$

Concrete stress at bottom fibre

$$\sigma_u = \frac{N}{A} + \frac{M}{I} y_u$$

$$= \frac{-71.45}{13.165} + \frac{-65.65}{66.820} \times 3.285$$

$$= -8.65 \text{ MN/m}^2$$

Concrete stress at top fibre in lower flange

$$\sigma_{fo} = \frac{-71.45}{13.165} + \frac{-65.65}{66.820} \times 2.785$$

$$= -8.16 \text{ MN/m}^2$$

See Fig. D20.

$$\bar{V}_S = \bar{V} - F_c \tan \gamma$$

$$= \bar{V} - \tfrac{1}{2}(\sigma_{fo} + \sigma_u)A_f \tan \gamma$$

$$= 10.56 - \tfrac{1}{2}(8.65 + 8.16) \times 2.557 \times 0.149$$

$$= 7.36 \text{ MN}$$

where A_f is taken as the area of the lower flange without the portion in the webs, since it is considered conservative.

$$\tau = \frac{7.36 \times 14.277}{1.212 \times 66.820} = 1.30 \text{ MN/m}^2$$

Therefore

$$\sigma_I = \frac{-5.43}{2} + \frac{1}{2} \sqrt{[(-5.43)^2 + 4 \times 1.30^2]}$$

$$= 0.30 \text{ MN/m}^2 \text{ (tension)}$$

$$\sigma_{ct \ lim} = 1.73 \text{ MN/m}^2 > 0.30 \text{ MN/m}^2$$

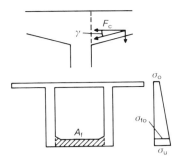

Fig. D20. Contribution of inclined compression chord

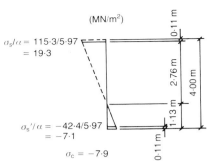

Fig. D21. Section 3: stresses at SLS (frequent combination during construction)

Section 2 (after construction of segment 27)

$M = -17 \cdot 15$ MN m

$N = -34 \cdot 19$ MN

$V = 0 \cdot 14$ MN

Concrete stress at top fibre

$\sigma = -2 \cdot 28$ MN/m^2 (compression) < 0 MN/m^2

Section 3 (after construction of segment 25)

$M = -70 \cdot 82$ MN m

$N = -22 \cdot 09$ MN

$V = 0$

Tensile stress calculated as an uncracked section

$\sigma_{ct} = 2 \cdot 96$ MN/m$^2 > 0 \cdot 7 f_{ctm} = 2 \cdot 17$ MN/m^2

Therefore the stresses are calculated for a cracked section.

Tensile steel stress (Fig. D16)

$\sigma_s = 115 \cdot 3$ MN/m^2

See Fig. D21.

Cracking moment

$$M_r = \left\{ 0 \cdot 7 f_{ctm} - \frac{N}{A} \right\} \frac{I}{y_o} = -\left\{ 2 \cdot 17 - \frac{-22 \cdot 09}{18 \cdot 80} \right\} \frac{34 \cdot 269}{2 \cdot 0}$$

$$= -57 \cdot 31 \text{ MN m}$$

Crack width   *5.5.4*

$$w_k \approx s\left(1 \cdot 5 + \frac{3 \cdot 5 c}{s} \right) \frac{\sigma_s}{E_s} \left(1 - \left\{ \frac{M_r}{M} \right\}^2 \right)$$

$$= 0 \cdot 125 \times \left(1 \cdot 5 + \frac{3 \cdot 5 \times 0 \cdot 0941}{0 \cdot 125} \right) \times \frac{115 \cdot 3}{2 \times 10^5} \times \left(1 - \left\{ \frac{-57 \cdot 31}{-70 \cdot 82} \right\}^2 \right)$$

$$= 1 \cdot 03 \times 10^{-4} \text{ m} = 0 \cdot 10 \text{ mm} < 0 \cdot 2 \text{ mm}$$

Section 4 (after construction of segment 25)

$M = -70 \cdot 82$ MN m

$N = -38 \cdot 99$ MN

$V = 0$

Tensile stress calculated as an uncracked section

$$\sigma_{ct} = 2\cdot40 \text{ MN/m}^2 > 0\cdot7 f_{ctm} = 2\cdot17 \text{ MN/m}^2$$

For a cracked section, tensile steel stress (Fig. D16)

$$\sigma_s = 35\cdot0 \text{ MN/m}^2$$

See Fig. D22.

Cracking moment

$$M_r = -66\cdot50 \text{ MN m}$$

Crack width

$$w_k \approx 1\cdot07 \times 10^{-5} \text{ m} = 0\cdot001 \text{ mm} < 0\cdot2 \text{ mm}$$

Table D10. Acting forces and moments at serviceability limit state: section 1 after completion

Action	Bending moment: MN m	Axial force: MN	Shear force: MN
Self-weight, G_0	−208·60	0·06	9·49
Prestress, P	187·46	−64·69	0·00
Surfacing, G_1	−34·66	−0·18	1·80
Redistribution due to creep, C	12·12	−0·36	−0·05
Shrinkage, S	0·95	0·23	0·00
Prestress loss, ΔP	−21·63	8·35	0·00
Live load, L	−72·21	−1·25	3·93
Temperature change, T	−0·99	−0·33	0·00
Earthquake, E	−65·92	−2·26	1·40
Frequent combination			
$G_0 + P + G_1 + C + S + \Delta P + 0\cdot5L$	−100·47	−57·21	13·20
$G_0 + P + G_1 + C + S + \Delta P + 0\cdot5T$	−64·85	−56·75	11·24
Infrequent combination			
$G_0 + P + G_1 + C + S + \Delta P + L + 0\cdot5T + 0\cdot5E$	−170·03	−59·13	15·87
$G_0 + P + G_1 + C + S + \Delta P + T + 0\cdot5E + 0\cdot5L$	−134·42	−58·67	13·90
$G_0 + P + G_1 + C + S + \Delta P + E + 0\cdot5L + 0\cdot5T$	−166·88	−59·64	14·60

Table D11. Acting forces and moments at serviceability limit state: section 2 after completion

Action	Bending moment: MN m	Axial force: MN	Shear force: MN
Self-weight, G_0	−0·98	0·06	0·14
Prestress, P	−17·38	−37·50	0·00
Surfacing, G_1	7·33	−0·18	0·04
Redistribution due to creep, C	9·77	−0·36	−0·05
Shrinkage, S	1·10	0·23	0·00
Prestress loss, ΔP	6·02	5·62	0·00
Live load, L	21·89	−2·26	0·60
Temperature change, T	1·08	0·33	0·00
Earthquake, E	2·18	−0·31	1·40
Frequent combination			
$G_0 + P + G_1 + C + S + \Delta P + 0\cdot5L$	16·80	−33·26	0·43
$G_0 + P + G_1 + C + S + \Delta P + 0\cdot5T$	6·40	−31·97	0·13
Infrequent combination			
$G_0 + P + G_1 + C + S + \Delta P + L + 0\cdot5T + 0\cdot5E$	29·38	−34·38	1·43
$G_0 + P + G_1 + C + S + \Delta P + T + 0\cdot5E + 0\cdot5L$	18·98	−33·09	1·13
$G_0 + P + G_1 + C + S + \Delta P + E + 0\cdot5L + 0\cdot5T$	19·53	−33·41	1·83

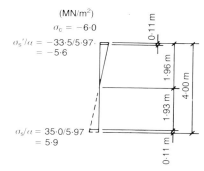

Fig. D22. Section 4: stresses at SLS (frequent combination during construction)

Table D12. *Acting forces and moments at serviceability limit state: section 3 after completion*

Action	Bending moment: MN m	Axial force: MN	Shear force: MN
Self-weight, G_0	$-21\cdot11$	$22\cdot92$	$0\cdot06$
Prestress, P	$-11\cdot99$	$-0\cdot28$	$1\cdot10$
Surfacing, G_1	$4\cdot72$	$-3\cdot61$	$-0\cdot18$
Redistribution due to creep, C	$12\cdot45$	$1\cdot15$	$-0\cdot35$
Shrinkage, S	$-2\cdot08$	$-0\cdot03$	$0\cdot23$
Prestress loss, ΔP	$4\cdot30$	$0\cdot05$	$-0\cdot21$
Live load, L	$-48\cdot21$	$-3\cdot70$	$-2\cdot26$
Temperature change, T	$-3\cdot72$	$-0\cdot06$	$0\cdot34$
Earthquake, E	$-90\cdot18$	$0\cdot77$	$-5\cdot32$
Frequent combination			
$G_0 + P + G_1 + C + S + \Delta P + 0\cdot5L$	$-37\cdot81$	$-27\cdot49$	$-0\cdot48$
$G_0 + P + G_1 + C + S + \Delta P + 0\cdot5T$	$-15\cdot57$	$-25\cdot67$	$0\cdot82$
Infrequent combination			
$G_0 + P + G_1 + C + S + \Delta P + L + 0\cdot5T + 0\cdot5E$	$-108\cdot87$	$-28\cdot99$	$-4\cdot10$
$G_0 + P + G_1 + C + S + \Delta P + T + 0\cdot5E + 0\cdot5L$	$-86\cdot62$	$-27\cdot17$	$-2\cdot80$
$G_0 + P + G_1 + C + S + \Delta P + E + 0\cdot5L + 0\cdot5T$	$-129\cdot85$	$-26\cdot75$	$-5\cdot63$

Table D13. *Acting forces and moments at serviceability limit state: section 4 after completion*

Action	Bending moment: MN m	Axial force: MN	Shear force: MN
Self-weight, G_0	$-18\cdot77$	$39\cdot83$	$0\cdot06$
Prestress, P	$30\cdot91$	$-0\cdot28$	$1\cdot10$
Surfacing, G_1	$-2\cdot30$	$-3\cdot61$	$-0\cdot18$
Redistribution due to creep, C	$-1\cdot20$	$1\cdot15$	$-0\cdot35$
Shrinkage, S	$6\cdot89$	$-0\cdot03$	$0\cdot23$
Prestress loss, ΔP	$-4\cdot04$	$0\cdot05$	$-0\cdot21$
Live load, L	$30\cdot53$	$-3\cdot71$	$-2\cdot26$
Temperature change, T	$9\cdot41$	$-0\cdot06$	$0\cdot34$
Earthquake, E	$166\cdot93$	$0\cdot77$	$-8\cdot20$
Frequent combination			
$G_0 + P + G_1 + C + S + \Delta P + 0\cdot5L$	$26\cdot75$	$-44\cdot40$	$-0\cdot48$
$G_0 + P + G_1 + C + S + \Delta P + 0\cdot5T$	$16\cdot19$	$-42\cdot58$	$0\cdot82$
Infrequent combination			
$G_0 + P + G_1 + C + S + \Delta P + L + 0\cdot5T + 0\cdot5E$	$130\cdot18$	$-45\cdot91$	$-5\cdot54$
$G_0 + P + G_1 + C + S + \Delta P + T + 0\cdot5E + 0\cdot5L$	$119\cdot62$	$-44\cdot08$	$-4\cdot24$
$G_0 + P + G_1 + C + S + \Delta P + E + 0\cdot5L + 0\cdot5T$	$198\cdot38$	$-43\cdot66$	$-8\cdot51$

D5.3. After completion

D5.3.1. Acting forces and moments

See Tables D10–D13.

D5.3.2. Compressive stresses in concrete *5.3.1*

Compressive stress in each section is obtained from the calculation for a cracked section under the infrequent combination of actions. (Sections 1 and 2 have rather high tensile stresses under the infrequent combination of actions, as shown below.)

Section 1 (Fig. D14)

Bending moment and axial force under infrequent combination

$$M = -170 \cdot 03 \text{ MN m}$$

$$N = -59 \cdot 13 \text{ MN}$$

Concrete stress at bottom fibre

$$\sigma_c = -13 \cdot 7 \text{ MN/m}^2$$

$$|\sigma_c| < 0 \cdot 5 f_{ck} = 20 \text{ MN/m}^2$$

See Fig. D23.

Section 2 (Fig. D15)

$$M = 29 \cdot 38 \text{ MN m}$$

$$N = -34 \cdot 38 \text{ MN}$$

$$\sigma_c = -9 \cdot 8 \text{ MN/m}^2$$

$$|\sigma_c| < 0 \cdot 5 f_{ck} = 20 \text{ MN/m}^2$$

See Fig. D24.

Section 3 (Fig. D16)

$$M = -129 \cdot 85 \text{ MN m}$$

$$N = -26 \cdot 75 \text{ MN}$$

$$\sigma_c = -14 \cdot 8 \text{ MN/m}^2$$

$$|\sigma_c| < 0 \cdot 5 f_{ck} = 17 \cdot 5 \text{ MN/m}^2$$

See Fig. D25.

Section 4 (Fig. D16)

$$M = 198 \cdot 38 \text{ MN m}$$

$$N = -43 \cdot 66 \text{ MN}$$

$$\sigma_c = -17 \cdot 4 \text{ MN/m}^2$$

$$|\sigma_c| < 0 \cdot 5 f_{ck} = 17 \cdot 5 \text{ MN/m}^2$$

See Fig. D26.

D5.3.3. Tensile stresses in concrete

Infrequent combination of actions.

Section 1 *3.4.3(a)*

Acting forces and moment under frequent combination

$$M = -100 \cdot 47 \text{ MN m}$$

$$N = -57 \cdot 21 \text{ MN}$$

$$V = 13 \cdot 20 \text{ MN}$$

Concrete stress at top fibre

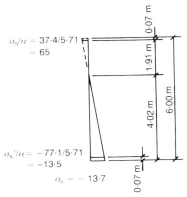

Fig. D23. Section 1: stresses at SLS (infrequent combination)

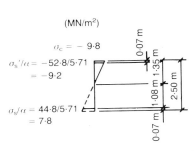

Fig. D24. Section 2: stresses at SLS (infrequent combination)

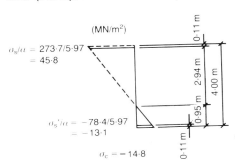

Fig. D25. Section 3: stresses at SLS (infrequent combination)

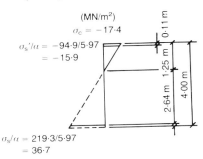

Fig. D26. Section 4: stresses at SLS (infrequent combination)

$$\sigma_{ct} = \frac{N}{A} - \frac{M}{I} y_o = \frac{-57 \cdot 21}{13 \cdot 165} - \frac{-100 \cdot 47}{66 \cdot 820} \times 2 \cdot 715$$

$$= -0 \cdot 26 \text{ MN/m}^2 \text{ (compression)} < 0 \text{ MN/m}^2$$

At centroid

$$\sigma_x = \frac{N}{A} = -4 \cdot 35 \text{ MN/m}^2$$

$$\sigma_y = 0$$

$$\sigma_u = 9 \cdot 25 \text{ MN/m}^2$$

$$\sigma_{fo} = 8 \cdot 52 \text{ MN/m}^2$$

$$V_S = 13 \cdot 20 - \tfrac{1}{2}(9 \cdot 25 + 8 \cdot 52) \times 2 \cdot 557 \times 0 \cdot 149 = 9 \cdot 81 \text{ MN}$$

$$\tau = \frac{9 \cdot 81 \times 14 \cdot 277}{1 \cdot 212 \times 66 \cdot 82} = 1 \cdot 73 \text{ MN/m}^2$$

Therefore

$$\sigma_1 = \frac{-4 \cdot 35}{2} + \frac{1}{2} \sqrt{[(-4 \cdot 35)^2 + 4 \times 1 \cdot 73^2]}$$

$$= 0 \cdot 60 \text{ MN/m}^2 \text{ (tension)}$$

Limit of principal stress

$$\sigma_{1\,lim} = 0 \cdot 75 f_{ctk} = 1 \cdot 73 \text{ MN/m}^2 > 0 \cdot 60 \text{ MN/m}^2$$

2.1.3
Fig. 2.2
3.4.3

Section 2

$$M = 16 \cdot 80 \text{ MN m}$$

$$N = -33 \cdot 26 \text{ MN}$$

$$V = 0.43 \text{ MN}$$

Concrete stress at bottom fibre

$$\sigma_{ct} = -0.21 \text{ MN/m}^2 \text{ (compression)} < 0 \text{ MN/m}^2$$

Section 3

$$M = -37.81 \text{ MN m}$$

$$N = -27.49 \text{ MN}$$

Tensile stress calculated as an uncracked section

$$\sigma_{ct} = 0.74 \text{ MN/m}^2 < 0.7 f_{ctm} = 2.17 \text{ MN/m}^2$$

However, considering the occurrence of possible cracking during construction, tensile steel stress is calculated for a cracked section (Fig. D16).

$$\sigma_s = 7.9 \text{ MN/m}^2$$

See Fig. D27.

It is reasonable that the cracking moment M_r is taken equal to the decompression moment here.

$$M_r = \frac{N}{A} \frac{I}{y_o}$$

$$= \frac{-27.49}{18.80} \times \frac{34.267}{2.0} = -25.05 \text{ MN m}$$

Crack width   *5.5.4*

$$w_k \approx s\left(1.5 + \frac{3.5c}{s}\right) \frac{\sigma_s}{E_s} \left(1 - \left\{\frac{M_r}{M}\right\}^2\right)$$

$$= 1.15 \times 10^{-5} \text{ m} = 0.01 \text{ mm} < 0.1 \text{ mm}$$

Section 4

$$M = 26.75 \text{ MN m}$$

$$N = -44.40 \text{ MN}$$

$$\sigma_{ct} = \frac{-44.0}{28.0} + \frac{26.75}{37.333} \times 2.0$$

$$= -0.15 \text{ MN/m}^2 \text{ (compression)} < 0 \text{ MN/m}^2$$

D5.4. Minimum reinforcement   *5.5.6*
Section 1

The section is under compression. However, to account for residual stresses, the top flange is considered as a tension flange ($h_{ef}/h_t = 0$).

(a) *Slab between webs*

Reinforcing bars 13 mm dia. at 100 mm centres and 16 mm dia. at 100 mm centres. See Fig. D28.

$$\rho_r = \frac{126.7 + 198.7}{300 \times 100} = 1.08 \times 10^{-2}$$

$$> \rho_{r\,min} = 0.44 \times 10^{-2} \qquad\qquad \textit{Fig. 5.5}$$

(b) *Cantilever*

Reinforcing bars 13 mm dia. at 200 mm centres and 13 mm dia. at 100 mm centres. Average slab thickness 350 mm. See Fig. D29.

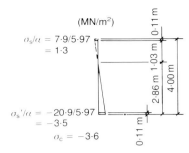

Fig. D27. Section 3: stresses at SLS (frequent combination)

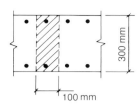

Fig. D28. Top slab between webs: effective area

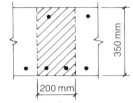

Fig. D29. Top slab cantilever: effective area

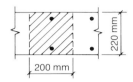

Fig. D30. Bottom slab: effective area

$$\rho_r = \frac{126 \cdot 7 + 2 \times 126 \cdot 7}{350 \times 200} = 0 \cdot 54 \times 10^{-2}$$

$$\approx \rho_{r\,min} = 0 \cdot 57 \times 10^{-2} \qquad \text{Fig. 5.5}$$

Section 2

The section is under compression. Nevertheless, a check of the bottom flange as a tension flange is carried out below ($h_{ef}/h_t = 0$).

Reinforcing bars 13 mm dia. at 200 mm centres. See Fig. D30.

$$\rho_r = \frac{126 \cdot 7 + 126 \cdot 7}{220 \times 200} = 0 \cdot 58 \times 10^{-2}$$

$$\approx \rho_{r\,min} = 0 \cdot 73 \times 10^{-2} \qquad \text{Fig. 5.5}$$

Section 3
Reinforcing bars 32 mm dia. at 125 mm centres.

$$\left.\begin{array}{l} h_{ef} \not> 200 \text{ mm} \\ h_t = 670 \text{ mm} \end{array}\right\} h_{ef}/h_t = 0 \cdot 3$$

$$\rho_r = \frac{794 \cdot 2}{200 \times 125} = 3 \cdot 18 \times 10^{-2} > \rho_{r\,min} = 0 \cdot 57 \times 10^{-2} \qquad \text{Fig. 5.5}$$

Section 4
Column section completely under compression. No check required.

Ultimate limit state

D6.1. Acting forces and moments
The ultimate limit state after completion is checked in this example. The values of the acting forces and moments are shown in Tables D14–D17.

D6.2. Flexure
D6.2.1. Resisting moment
  Section 1 (Fig. D14)
(a) *Assumptions*
    All tensile steel is yielding.
    Neutral axis is in web.

Table D14. Acting forces and moments at ultimate limit state: section 1

Action	Bending moment: MN m	Axial force: MN	Shear force: MN
Self-weight, G_0	− 208·60	0·06	9·49
Surfacing, G_1	− 34·66	− 0·18	1·80
Live load, L	− 70·78	− 2·26	3·93
Earthquake, E	− 65·92	− 2·26	1·40
$1·35(G_0 + G_1) + 1·5L + 1·5 \times 0·3E$	− 464·24	− 4·57	21·77
$1·35(G_0 + G_1) + 1·5E + 1·5 \times 0·3L$	− 459·13	− 4·57	19·11

Table D15. Acting forces and moments at ultimate limit state: section 2

Action	Bending moment: MN m	Axial force: MN	Shear force: MN
Self-weight, G_0	− 0·98	0·06	0·14
Surfacing, G_1	7·33	− 0·18	0·04
Live load, L	21·89	− 2·26	0·60
Earthquake, E	0·42	0·31	1·40
$1·35(G_0 + G_1) + 1·5L + 1·5 \times 0·3E$	41·60	− 3·41	1·77
$1·35(G_0 + G_1) + 1·5E + 1·5 \times 0·3L$	19·05	− 0·71	2·61

Table D16. Acting forces and moments at ultimate limit state: section 3

Action	Bending moment: MN m	Axial force: MN	Shear force: MN
Self-weight, G_0	− 21·11	− 22·92	0·06
Surfacing, G_1	4·72	− 3·61	− 0·18
Live load, L	55·01	− 4·13	− 2·26
Earthquake, E	90·18	− 0·77	− 5·32
$1·35(G_0 + G_1) + 1·5L + 1·5 \times 0·3E$	100·97	− 42·36	− 5·95
$1·35(G_0 + G_1) + 1·5E + 1·5 \times 0·3L$	137·90	− 38·83	− 9·16

Table D17. Acting forces and moments at ultimate limit state: section 4

Action	Bending moment: MN m	Axial force: MN	Shear force: MN
Self-weight, G_0	− 18·77	− 39·83	0·06
Surfacing, G_1	− 2·30	− 3·61	− 0·18
Live load, L	− 35·77	− 4·14	− 2·26
Earthquake, E	− 166·93	− 0·77	− 8·20
$1·35(G_0 + G_1) + 1·5L + 1·5 \times 0·3E$	− 157·22	− 65·20	− 7·24
$1·35(G_0 + G_1) + 1·5E + 1·5 \times 0·3L$	− 294·94	− 61·66	− 13·48

Table D18. Section 1: steel tensile forces at ultimate limit state

	Steel	d_s: m	A_s: m^2	$f_s/1·15$: MN/m^2	F_s: MN
Reinforcement	{133 bars of 13 mm dia.} { 47 bars of 16 mm dia.}	5·85	0·026 19	348	9·11
Prestressing	140 bars of 32 mm dia.	5·63	0·110 5	696	76·86
					85·97

(b) *Steel tensile forces at ultimate limit state*
   See Table D18.
(c) *Concrete compressive force at ultimate limit state*

$$F_c = 0.8 \times \frac{40}{1.5} \{4.974 \times 0.5 + 0.35 \times 0.20 + 1.212 \times 0.8x\}$$

$$= -N + F_s$$

$$= 4.57 + 85.97 = 90.54 \text{ MN}$$

Neutral axis (from bottom): $x = 1.749$ m

Axis of F_c (from bottom)

$$b = (4.974 \times 0.5 \times 0.25 + 0.35 \times 0.20 \times 0.567$$
$$+ 1.212 \times 1.399 \times 0.700)/(4.974 \times 0.5 + 0.35 \times 0.20$$
$$+ 1.212 \times 1.399)$$
$$= 0.435 \text{ m}$$

(d) *Resisting moments about centroid*

$$M_R = 9.11(5.85 - 3.285) + 76.86(5.63 - 3.285)$$
$$+ 90.54(3.285 - 0.435)$$
$$= 23.37 + 180.24 + 258.04$$
$$= 461.65 \text{ MN m}$$

(e) *Strain condition check*
   Extreme compressive fibre: $\varepsilon_c = -3.5 \times 10^{-3}$

Reinforcing steel

$$\varepsilon_s = \frac{5.85 - 1.749}{1.749} \times 3.5 \times 10^{-3} = 8.20 \times 10^{-3} \rightarrow \text{yielding}$$

Prestressing steel

$$\varepsilon_p = \varepsilon_{pt} + \Delta\varepsilon_p$$

$$= \frac{0.470}{2.0 \times 10^5 \times 7.89 \times 10^{-4}} + \frac{5.63 - 1.749}{1.749} \times 3.5 \times 10^{-3}$$

$$= 2.98 \times 10^{-3} + 7.77 \times 10^{-3} = 10.76 \times 10^{-3} \rightarrow \text{yielding}$$

Section 2 (Fig. D15)
(a) *Assumptions*
   All tensile steel is yielding.
   Neutral axis is in flange.
(b) *Steel tensile forces at ultimate limit state*
   See Table D19.
(c) *Concrete compressive force at ultimate limit state*

$$F_c = 0.8 \times \frac{40}{1.5} \times 11.2 \times 0.8x = -N + F_s$$

$$= 3.41 + 50.88 = 54.29 \text{ MN}$$

Table D19. Section 2: steel tensile forces at ultimate limit state

	Steel	d_s: m	A_s: m^2	$f_s/1.15$: MN/m^2	F_s: MN
Reinforcement	58 bars of 13 mm dia.	2.39	0.007 349	348	2.56
Prestressing	88 bars of 32 mm dia.	2.29	0.069 43	696	48.32
					50.88

Neutral axis (from top): $x = 0.284$ m

Axis of F_c (from top): $b = 0.4x = 0.114$ m

(d) *Resisting moments about centroid*

$$M_R = 2.56(2.39 - 0.898) + 48.32(2.29 - 0.898)$$
$$+ 54.29(0.898 - 0.114)$$
$$= 3.82 + 67.26 + 42.56$$
$$= 113.64 \text{ MN m}$$

(e) *Strain condition check*
Reinforcing steel: $\varepsilon_s = 10 \times 10^{-3}$

Extreme compressive fibre

$$\varepsilon_c = \frac{-0.284}{2.39 - 0.284} \times 10 \times 10^{-3} = -1.35 \times 10^{-3}$$

$$|\varepsilon_c| < 3.5 \times 10^{-3}$$

Prestressing steel

$$\varepsilon_p = \varepsilon_{pt} + \Delta\varepsilon_p$$

$$= \frac{0.440}{2.0 \times 10^5 \times 7.89 \times 10^{-4}} + \frac{2.29 - 0.284}{2.39 - 0.284} \times 10 \times 10^{-3}$$

$$= 2.79 \times 10^{-3} + 9.52 \times 10^{-3} = 12.31 \times 10^{-3} \rightarrow \text{yielding}$$

Section 3 (Fig. D16)

(a) *Assumptions*
All tensile steel is yielding ($\varepsilon_s = 10 \times 10^{-3}$).
Neutral axis is in flange; compression steel not yielding.

(b) *Steel tensile force at ultimate limit state*

$$d_s = 3.75 \text{ m}$$
$$A_s = 0.0804 \text{ m}^2 \text{ (64 at 32 mm dia., 46 at 29 mm dia.)}$$
$$F_s = 0.0804 \times 348 = 27.98 \text{ MN}$$

(c) *Steel and concrete compressive forces at ultimate limit state*

$$d'_s = 0.25 \text{ m}$$
$$A'_s = 0.0804 \text{ m}^2$$

$$F'_s = 0.0804 \times \frac{x - 0.25}{3.75 - x} \times 10 \times 10^{-3} \times 2.0 \times 10^5$$

$$F_c = 0.8 \times \frac{35}{1.5} \times 7.0 \times 0.8x$$

$$F'_s + F_c = N + F_s = 38.83 + 27.98 = 66.81 \text{ MN}$$

Neutral axis: $x = 0.514$ m

Axis of F_c: $b = 0.4x = 0.206$ m

$$F'_s = 13.11 \text{ MN}$$
$$F_c = 53.70 \text{ MN}$$

(d) *Resisting moments about centroid*

$$M_R = 27.98(3.75 - 2.0) + 13.11(2.0 - 0.25) + 53.70(2.0 - 0.206)$$
$$= 48.97 + 22.94 + 96.34$$
$$= 168.25 \text{ MN m}$$

(e) *Strain condition check*
Tensile steel: $\varepsilon_s = 10 \times 10^{-3}$

Compressive steel

$$\varepsilon'_s = -\frac{0.514 - 0.25}{3.75 - 0.514} \times 10 \times 10^{-3}$$

$$= -0.82 \times 10^{-3} \rightarrow \text{not yielding}$$

Extreme compressive fibre

$$\varepsilon_c = -\frac{0.514}{3.75 - 0.514} \times 10 \times 10^{-3} = -1.59 \times 10^{-3}$$

$$|\varepsilon_c| < 3.5 \times 10^{-3}$$

Section 4 (Fig. D16)

(a) *Assumption*
All tensile steel is yielding.

(b) *Steel tensile force at ultimate limit state*

$$d_s = 3.70 \text{ m}$$

$$A_s = 0.1398 \text{ m}^2 \text{ (20 at 35 mm dia., 152 at 32 mm dia.)}$$

$$F_s = 0.1398 \times 348 = 52.50 \text{ MN}$$

(c) *Steel and concrete compressive forces at ultimate limit state*

$$d'_s = 0.3 \text{ m}$$

$$A'_s = 0.1398 \text{ m}^2$$

$$F'_s = 0.1398 \times \frac{x - 0.3}{3.7 - x} \times 10 \times 10^{-3} \times 2.0 \times 10^5$$

$$F_c = 0.8 \times \frac{35}{1.5} \times 7.0 \times 0.8x$$

$$F'_s + F_c = -N + F_s = 61.66 + 52.50 = 114.16 \text{ MN}$$

Neutral axis: $x = 0.718 \text{ m}$

Axis of F_c: $b = 0.4x = 0.287 \text{ m}$

$$F'_s = 39.15 \text{ MN}$$

$$F_c = 75.01 \text{ MN}$$

(d) *Resisting moments about centroid*

$$M_R = 52.50(3.7 - 2.0) + 39.15(2.0 - 0.3) + 75.01(2.0 - 0.287)$$

$$= 89.25 + 66.56 + 128.49$$

$$= 284.30 \text{ MN m}$$

(e) *Strain condition check*
Tensile steel: $\varepsilon_s = 10 \times 10^{-3}$

Compressive steel

$$\varepsilon'_s = -\frac{0.718 - 0.3}{3.7 - 0.718} \times 10 \times 10^{-3}$$

$$= -1.40 \times 10^{-3} \rightarrow \text{not yielding}$$

Extreme compressive fibre

$$\varepsilon_c = -\frac{0.718}{3.7 - 0.718} \times 10 \times 10^{-3} = -2.41 \times 10^{-3}$$

$$|\varepsilon_c| < 3.5 \times 10^{-3}$$

D6.2.2. Checks
  Girder (Fig. D31)

$$M_{S0} = M_{S1} + M_{S2}$$

(a) *Condition to be fulfilled:* $M_{S0} < M_{R1} + M_{R2}$ 4.2.2

$$M_{S0} = 464 \cdot 24 + 41 \cdot 60 = 505 \cdot 84 \text{ MN m}$$

$$M_{R1} + M_{R2} = 461 \cdot 65 + 113 \cdot 64 = 575 \cdot 29 \text{ MN m} > M_{S0}$$

(b) *Ductility condition at section 1:* $\rho < 0 \cdot 02$ 4.2.4
  Reinforcing steel in flange

$$A_{sf} = 0 \cdot 02619 \text{ m}^2$$

$$d_{sf} = 5 \cdot 85 \text{ m}$$

  Reinforcing steel in web within tension zone

$$A_{sw} = 0 \cdot 01926 \text{ m}^2 \text{ (148 at 13 mm dia.)}$$

$$d_{sw} = 3 \cdot 58 \text{ m}$$

  Prestressing steel

$$A_p = 0 \cdot 1105 \text{ m}^2$$

$$d_p = 5 \cdot 63 \text{ m}$$

$$\rho = \frac{1}{b_{av}} \left\{ \frac{A_{sf}}{d_{sf}} + \frac{A_{sw}}{d_{sw}} + \frac{A_p}{d_p} \times \frac{f_{0 \cdot 1k}}{f_{yk}} \right\}$$

  where b_{av} is average width of compression zone

$$b_{av} = \frac{4 \cdot 974 \times 0 \cdot 5 + 0 \cdot 35 \times 0 \cdot 20 + 1 \cdot 212 \times 1 \cdot 749}{1 \cdot 749}$$

$$= 2 \cdot 674 \text{ m}$$

$$\rho = \frac{1}{2 \cdot 674} \left\{ \frac{0 \cdot 02619}{5 \cdot 85} + \frac{0 \cdot 01926}{3 \cdot 58} + \frac{0 \cdot 1105 \times 800}{5 \cdot 63 \times 400} \right\}$$

$$= 0 \cdot 018 < 0 \cdot 02$$

(c) *Mechanical degree of prestressing (for information)*   3.1.2
  Section 1

$$\lambda = \frac{76 \cdot 86}{76 \cdot 86 + 9 \cdot 11} = 0 \cdot 89$$

  Section 2

$$\lambda = \frac{48 \cdot 32}{48 \cdot 32 + 2 \cdot 56} = 0 \cdot 95$$

  Pier (Fig. D32)

$$M_{S0} = M_{S3} + M_{S4}$$

(a) *Condition to be fulfilled:* $M_{S0} < M_{R3} + M_{R4}$ 4.2.2

$$M_{S0} = 137 \cdot 90 + 294 \cdot 94 = 432 \cdot 84 \text{ MN m}$$

$$M_{R3} + M_{R4} = 168 \cdot 25 + 281 \cdot 37 = 449 \cdot 62 \text{ MN m} > M_{S0}$$

(b) *Ductility condition at section 4:* $\rho < 0 \cdot 02$ 4.2.4

$$\rho = \frac{A_s}{bd} = \frac{0 \cdot 1398}{7 \cdot 0 \times 3 \cdot 70} = 0 \cdot 005 < 0 \cdot 02$$

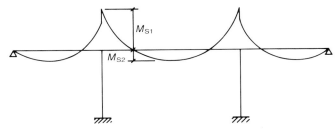

Fig. D31. Definitions for ULS check of girder

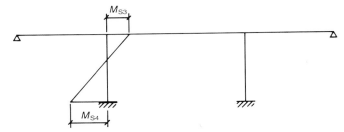

Fig. D32. Definitions for ULS check of pier

D6.3. Shear

In this example, section 1 is checked without consideration of the favourable effect of σ_y near the support, to show the calculation simply.

4.4.2

Acting forces and moment under the loading condition which gives the maximum shear force

$$M = -448\cdot30 \text{ MN m}$$

$$N = -0\cdot36 \text{ MN}$$

$$V = 21\cdot77 \text{ MN}$$

Lower flange is compressed.

Bottom fibre

$$\sigma_u = \frac{N}{A} + \frac{M}{I}\, y_u = \frac{-0\cdot36}{13\cdot165} + \frac{-448\cdot30}{66\cdot820} \times 3\cdot285$$

$$= -22\cdot07 \text{ MN/m}^2$$

Top fibre in lower flange

$$\sigma_{fo} = \frac{-0\cdot36}{13\cdot165} + \frac{-448\cdot30}{66\cdot820} \times 2\cdot785 = -18\cdot71 \text{ MN/m}^2$$

Lower flange inclination

$$\frac{6\cdot0 - 5\cdot559}{2\cdot95} = 0\cdot149$$

Design shear force

$$V_{Sd} = 21\cdot77 - \tfrac{1}{2}(22\cdot07 + 18\cdot71) \times 2\cdot557 \times 0\cdot149$$

$$= 14\cdot00 \text{ MN}$$

Upper limit of resistant shear force

$$V_{Rd} = V_{Rd2} + A_p \sigma_p \sin \alpha_p$$

$$V_{Rd2} = 0\cdot30 f_{cd} b_w d$$

$$= 0\cdot30 \times \frac{40}{1\cdot5} \times 1\cdot212 \times 5\cdot63 = 54\cdot59 \text{ MN}$$

$$\sin \alpha_p = 0$$

Therefore

$$V_{Rd} = V_{Rd2} > V_{Sd}$$

Resistant shear force provided by concrete

$$V_{cd} = 2 \cdot 5\tau_{Rd} \, b_{wd} \left\{ 1 + \frac{M_o}{M_{Sdu}} \right\}$$

$$\tau_{Rd} = 0 \cdot 42 \text{ MN/m}^2$$

$$M_{Sdu} = 448 \cdot 30 \text{ MN m}$$

Table

Decompression moment (see section 11.1.2.2 of MC78)

$$M_o = \frac{I}{y_o} \left\{ \frac{N^*}{A} + \frac{M^*}{I} \, y_o \right\}$$

$$N^* = 0 \cdot 9 \times (-64 \cdot 69 + 8 \cdot 35) \qquad \text{(prestress (loss included))}$$

$$+ 1 \cdot 0 \times 0 \cdot 06 \qquad \text{(self-weight)}$$

$$+ 1 \cdot 0 \times (-0 \cdot 18) \qquad \text{(surfacing)}$$

$$= -50 \cdot 83 \text{ MN}$$

In the estimation of N^*, the coefficients of favourable effects ($\gamma_g = 1 \cdot 0$, $\gamma_p = 0 \cdot 9$) are considered.

$$M^* = 0 \cdot 9 \times (187 \cdot 46 - 21 \cdot 63) \qquad \text{(prestress)}$$

$$= 149 \cdot 25 \text{ MN m}$$

Therefore

$$M_o = \frac{66 \cdot 820}{2 \cdot 715} \left\{ \frac{50 \cdot 83}{13 \cdot 165} + \frac{149 \cdot 25}{66 \cdot 820} \times 2 \cdot 715 \right\} = 244 \cdot 27 \text{ MN m}$$

$$1 + \frac{M_o}{M_{Sdu}} = 1 \cdot 545 < 2 \cdot 0$$

$$V_{cd} = 2 \cdot 5 \times 0 \cdot 42 \times 1 \cdot 212 \times 5 \cdot 63 \times 1 \cdot 545 = 11 \cdot 07 \text{ MN}$$

Resistant shear force provided by stirrups (dia. 13 mm, $s = 250$ mm)

$$V_{wd} = 0 \cdot 9d \, \frac{A_{sw}}{s} \, f_{ywd}$$

$$= 0 \cdot 9 \times 5 \cdot 63 \times 20 \cdot 27 \times 10^{-4} \times \frac{400}{1 \cdot 15} = 3 \cdot 57 \text{ MN}$$

Therefore

$$V_{Sd} < V_{cd} + V_{wd} = 14 \cdot 64 \text{ MN}$$

$$\rho_w = \frac{A_{sw}}{s b_w} = \frac{20 \cdot 27 \times 10^{-4}}{1 \cdot 212} = 0 \cdot 0016 > \rho_{min} = 0 \cdot 0015$$

Reference

1. Japan Road Association. *Specifications for highway bridges—Part III. Concrete bridges.* 1978.

Eimeikan Bridge, Tokyo, Japan: two-span cable-stayed bridge

Cantilever method with adjustment of stay cables

Example prepared by Y. Imai (Tokyo), with the assistance of J. Almeida (Lisbon) and D. Lee (London)

References to *FIP recommendations: Practical design of reinforced and prestressed concrete structures (based on the CEB–FIP model code (MC78))* are given in the right-hand margin

. Cable-stayed idges

E1.1. General description

Cable-stayed bridges are structural systems in which inclined stay cables act as tension members supporting the bridge deck directly.

A large number of stays is in general the best solution. A small number of stays results in large cable forces. These require complicated anchorage systems and detailing, and a relatively rigid deck is required to span the distance between anchorage points. In addition, erection of concrete cable-stayed bridges by the cantilever method is much simpler if the cable spacing is small.

The cantilever method is in general very suitable for the erection of concrete cable-stayed bridges. In particular cases, in general in the range of small spans, traditional methods of construction may prove to be more economical.

E1.2. Actions

When the cantilever method is used, geometric control during construction is essential. Particular attention must be given to the control of dead loads during the erection phase. The correlation between analysis and construction is highly dependent on the accuracy of the dead load values.

Also, the effects of temperature during the construction phase can be relevant in long-span structures. For such structures, a straightforward method for correcting the cable forces is required.

Stays, in particular backstay cables, may be subjected to important variations of stresses. If relevant, fatigue loads must be evaluated on the basis of traffic measurements.

Reduction of the traffic live load values can be adopted in the design of long cable-stayed bridges, as proposed in Appendix 1 of the recommendations.

Long-span cable-stayed bridges may be sensitive to aerodynamic effects. In such cases, local wind conditions must be carefully evaluated.

E1.3. Design principles

E1.3.1. Introduction

The cables in tension provide intermediate elastic supports for the bridge deck and introduce compression in the pylons and deck.

Under permanent actions, the cable forces must be adjusted in order to obtain the required bridge profile and the optimum distribution of the internal forces. Under traffic loadings, the deck distributes the loads between the stays, which work as elastic supports. The distribution of internal forces is dependent on the relative stiffnesses of the various elements. Particular attention must be given to the stiffness distribution adopted for the structural elements.

E1.3.2. Structural analysis

In many cases, elastic analysis of the structure can be used. Nevertheless, concrete cable-stayed bridges can be sensitive to non-linear effects.

The principal sources of non-linearity in concrete cable-stayed bridges are the following.

(a) Long cables sag under their own weight, the amount of sag being a function of the stay tension. Owing to the ratio of live to dead load usual in concrete cable-stayed bridges, this effect will, in general, be relevant only for very long cables. Particular attention must be given to the load cases which significantly unload the stays, where the loss of stiffness of these elements can be relevant.

(b) The deck and the pylons are in general subjected to important axial forces. In many cases they consist of slender elements. If deformations are relatively large, second order effects may be important, and the equilibrium conditions should be established for the deformed configuration.

(c) Material non-linear effects of the concrete elements can change the relative stiffnesses of the various elements significantly. It may be necessary to evaluate the effect on the load-bearing behaviour of the structure.

In each case the designer must identify the relevant sources of non-linearity. If necessary, adequate techniques of non-linear analysis must be used.

Long-span cable-stayed bridges can be sensitive to aerodynamic effects. In this case, conceptual aspects improving aerodynamic behaviour should be implemented, and safety checked by appropriate analytical and experimental methods of dynamic analysis.

In seismic regions, particular attention should be given to the support of the deck, in order to reduce the dynamic response of the structure. In many cases the natural frequencies are such that earthquake effects are not critical.

E1.3.3. Serviceability limit state
In many cases serviceability is the main criterion for checking the safety of this type of structure.

Adjustment of the stays
The proper adjustment of the stays directly controls the deformations under permanent actions. The adjustment of the backstay cables makes it possible to position the pylons so that they are not subjected to significant bending moments under permanent actions.

Deformations
Cable-stayed bridges can be flexible structures. Limits to the deflection values must only depend on traffic requirements, which are in general independent of the maximum deflection under total live load.

In general, physiological vibration effects are not a critical problem. If relevant, they must be checked by appropriate methods.

Crack control
Prestressing in the stays introduces compression forces in the deck and the pylons that, in general, ensure that no decompression occurs under frequent combinations of actions.

Additional prestress is needed in the zones where 'natural' prestressing by the stays is not present or is insufficient.

In segmental construction with prefabricated elements, with no longitudinal reinforcement across the joints, a higher degree of prestressing is necessary, especially if unbonded external tendons are used.

Transverse prestressing should be used for the transverse bending if necessary, and for the transverse normal forces due to the dispersion in the deck of the horizontal forces introduced by the stays. In central suspension systems, where torsional rigidity of the section is required, transverse prestressing should also be used to counteract torsional stresses.

Cracking under rare combinations of actions should be controlled by limiting the steel stresses, according to section 5.5.5 of the recommendations.

A minimum amount of reinforcement should be provided and careful detailing adopted. Particular attention should be given to the stay anchorages.

E1.3.4. Ultimate limit state
Combination of actions

The acting internal forces should be determined with the partial safety factors presented in section 4.1.2 of the recommendations.

For the partial coefficient for the permanent actions, a single value of 1·35 can in general be taken throughout the structure, or 1·0 when its effect is favourable.

In particular cases, when some unfavourable part of this action needs to be considered individually, specific γ_g values should be defined. This applies in particular to the check of the general equilibrium.

For a regular check, the principles of the theory of plasticity should be applied. As a simplification, dead loads and prestressing in the stays may be considered as independent actions. Internal forces due to the adjustment of the cables correspond to the effects of a predeformation of the stays. For this 'load condition' (in fact, an imposed deformation), a γ coefficient of 1·0 can be considered. Nevertheless, due to the fact that dead load and stay-cable tension are in equilibrium, a unique coefficient may be applied to dead load and stay-cable tension.

If relevant, the pylons have to be designed taking into account the non-linear effects.

In the transverse direction—critical if the pylons are formed of slender elements not braced in this direction—the second order influence of the longitudinal stays, counteracting the transverse displacements, should be considered.

In the longitudinal direction, the slenderness of the pylons depends on the stiffness and distribution of the stays, mainly the backstay cables, and on the rigidity of the deck. With slender decks, and if the static system does not provide intermediate supports in the lateral spans, it may be necessary to take into account the non-linear behaviour of the entire system.

General equilibrium

At the end supports, vertical uplift reactions must be anchored. These forces depend primarily on the ratio between central and side spans. A similar situation occurs when backstay cables are anchored in a counterweight or even directly anchored in the ground.

General equilibrium must be checked according to section 4.7 of the recommendations. The uplift reactions can increase significantly if cracking occurs at the base of the pylons.

Design of the stay cables

For the design of the stays, both the resistance and the fatigue criteria must be considered.

The resistance check is traditionally stated as a stress limit condition for service loads. Maximum stresses in the stays, under service loads, of about 45% of the ultimate steel stress are in general adopted. Future design criteria should be based on the partial safety factors for actions and resistance, which will probably result in a less restrictive condition.

Safety against fatigue should be checked according to section 4.8 of the recommendations. The characteristic fatigue strength should be evaluated on the basis of test results.

For concrete cable-stayed bridges carrying highways, fatigue is not, in general, the governing criterion in the design of the stays. Even in these cases, systems with well proved performance concerning fatigue resistance should be used.

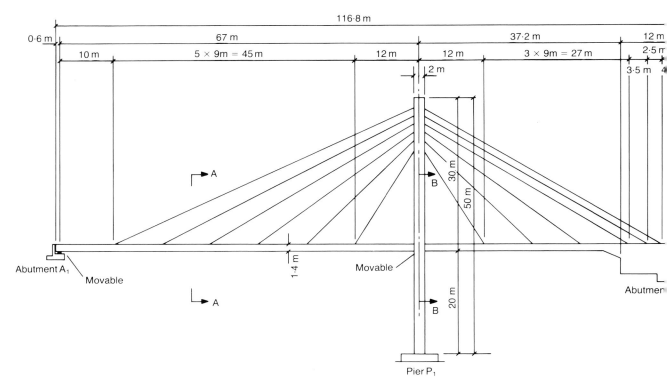

Fig. E1. Elevation

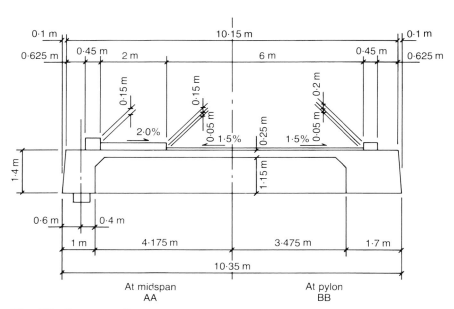

Fig. E2. Cross-sections

E2. Design information

E2.1. Structural summary

The structure is 116·80 m in total length and 10·35 m wide. It has two spans and a continuous girder. The span lengths are 67·00 m and 37·20 m (Fig. E1).

At one end, the bridge girder is movable and supported on an abutment; at the other end it is monolithically fixed in a concrete block which acts as a counterweight. The superstructure consists of a 250 mm deep slab, stiffened at each edge with a post-tensioned longitudinal girder 1·40 m deep. The width of the girders varies from 1·00 m to 1·70 m. Every 4·5 m the cross-section is stiffened with a transverse beam (Fig. E2).

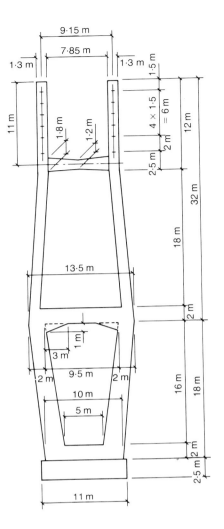

Fig. E3. Pylon

The concrete pylon carries two planes of fan-shaped cables anchored to the edge beams. The total height of the pylon from the top of the foundation is 50·00 m. The pylon has two transverse beams and the superstructure is supported on the lower beam (Fig. E3).

Concrete for the girder was cast on a scaffold.

E2.2. Materials
Concrete

Superstructure and pylon	C40
Pier	C30

Reinforcing steel S400
Prestressing steel and stay-cable strands SWPR 7B-12, dia. 15·2 mm.

E2.3. Loading conditions
Permanent load

Concrete density (containing steel)	25 kN/m^3
Surfacing (in longitudinal direction)	30·34 kN/m

Live load (type H$_1$, normal) *App.1*

Uniformly distributed load	4·5 kN/m^2
Concentrated load	300 kN

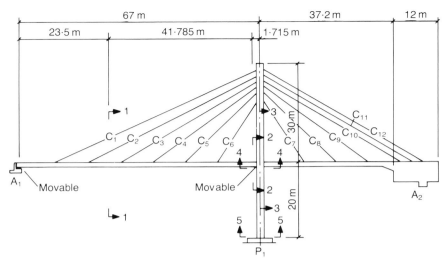

Fig. E4. Notation

Pedestrian	$3 \cdot 0 \ \text{kN/m}^2$
Seismic coefficient	$0 \cdot 23$

According to the Japan Road Association's *Specifications for road bridges*,[1] the seismic coefficient is defined using the formula

$$\kappa_h = v_1 v_2 v_3 \kappa_0$$

where κ_h is the coefficient for design horizontal seismic force, κ_0 is the coefficient for basic horizontal seismic force (generally about 0·2), v_1 is the seismic zone factor (generally 0·7–1·0), v_2 is the ground condition factor (generally 0·9–1·2), and v_3 is the factor for considering the natural period of the structure (0·5–1·25).

In this example

$$\kappa_h = 1 \cdot 0 \times 0 \cdot 9 \times 1 \cdot 25 \times 0 \cdot 2$$
$$= 0 \cdot 23$$

Temperature
(a) For whole structure $\pm 15°C$
(b) For stay cables only $+ 10°C$
(c) For upper side of slab only $+ 5°C$
(d) Combinations of (a), (b) and (c).

In this example, the wind force is smaller than the seismic force and is therefore omitted.

E2.4. Serviceability conditions
Concrete in compression   *5.3.1*
Under infrequent combinations of actions, the concrete in compression is checked

$$\sigma_{cc} \leqslant 0 \cdot 5 f_{ck}$$

Concrete in tension   *5.3.2*
Under frequent combinations of actions, the principal diagonal tensile stress should be limited.

Crack control   *5.5*
Under frequent combinations of actions, the crack width should be checked

Exposure—normal: allowable crack width $w < 0 \cdot 1$ mm

E2.5. Sections checked in the example

Five critical sections are checked. Sections 1 and 3–5 (Fig. E4) are checked for bending moment. Section 2, checked for shear, is located at the section of effective depth *d* from the face of the direct support.

The axial forces of four stay cables are checked.

3. Basic data

E3.1 Materials

Concrete

See Table E1.

Reinforcing steel S400

Strength: $f_{yk} = 400$ N/mm^2

E-modulus: $E_s = 200$ kN/mm^2

Prestressing steel and stay cable

Characteristic strength: $f_{0\cdot1k} = 1537$ N/mm^2

Tensile strength: $f_{tk} = 1862$ N/mm^2

Relaxation 5%

E-modulus: $E_s = 200$ kN/mm^2

Soil

Density of soil: $\gamma = 19$ kN/m^3

Cohesion: $c = 0$

Friction angle: $Q_0 = 12\cdot95°$

Design bearing capacity

    Normal 600 kN/m^2

    Seismic 900 kN/m^2

Coefficient of friction between concrete and soil: $\mu = 0\cdot6$

E3.2. Loading

Stay-cable tension

Tensions in stay cables are shown in Table E2. These tensions are under the loads of self-weight, surfacing, and adjustment of stay-cable tensions. The values of adjustment of cable tensions are determined on the assumption that the moment distribution is almost the same as for the continuous beam supported by stay cables. Under the same conditions, the moment of the pylon is reduced by back-stay cables which are anchored to abutment A_2.

Live load

Maximum section force by live load is calculated using influence-line theory.

Creep and shrinkage

Table E3 shows the age of concrete for calculating the forces due to creep and shrinkage.

Table E1. Concrete data

	C40	C30
Compressive strength, f_{ck}: N/mm^2	40	30
Tensile strength, f_{ctm}: N/mm^2	3·4	2·8
E-modulus, E_{cm}: kN/mm^2	35	32

Fig. 2.2
Fig. 2.3

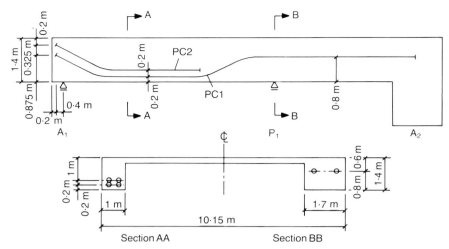

Fig. E5. Arrangement of tendons in girder

E3.3. Prestress (in girder)

Two types of prestressing cables are used in the girder

PC1—tensioning from both sides

PC2—tensioning from side A_1 only

Strands: SWPR 7B-12, dia. 15·2 mm

$A_p = 1664\cdot4$ mm^2

The prestressing forces at each section (Fig. E5) are calculated by computer.

Table E2. Tensions in stay cables

Stay cable*	Number of strands		Sectional area of stay cables for two planes: mm^2	Tension: kN
	In one cable	In two planes		
C1	26	52	7212	4302·2
C2	20	40	5548	3155·6
C3	20	40	5548	3018·4
C4	18	36	4993	2675·4
C5	13	26	3606	2009·0
C6	15	30	4161	2391·2
C7	15	30	4161	2391·2
C8	13	26	3606	1979·6
C9	16	32	4438	2548·0
C10	23	46	6380	3675·0
C11	23	46	6380	3675·0
C12	23	46	6380	3675·0

* See Fig. E4.

Table E3. Concrete age at the moment of tensioning

	Age of concrete: days
Pier	150
Pylon	100
Superstructure	
P_1 to A_2	60
A_1 to P_1	30

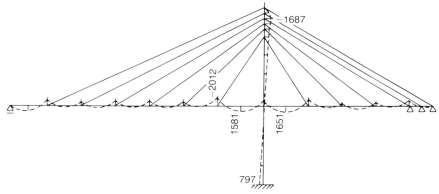

Fig. E6. Bending moments (kNm): dead load and adjustment of forces in stay cables

Maximum tension stress at the moment of tensioning *3.2.1*
Tension at the front of the jack is $P_i = 2254 \cdot 0$ kN.

$$\sigma_{p\,max} = \frac{P_i}{A_p} = \frac{2254 \cdot 0 \times 10^3}{1664 \cdot 4}$$

$$= 1354 \text{ N/mm}^2$$

$$0 \cdot 80 f_{tk} = 0 \cdot 80 \times 1862 \text{ N/mm}^2 = 1490 \text{ N/mm}^2$$

$$0 \cdot 90 f_{0 \cdot 1k} = 0 \cdot 90 \times 1537 \text{ N/mm}^2 = 1383 \text{ N/mm}^2$$

$$\left. \begin{array}{l} \sigma_{p\,max} < 0 \cdot 80 f_{tk} \\ \sigma_{p\,max} < 0 \cdot 90 f_{0 \cdot 1k} \end{array} \right\} \text{(OK)}$$

Immediate losses *3.3.2*
(*a*) Due to friction

$$\Delta\sigma_{pi} = \sigma_{pi}\{1 - \exp[-\mu(\alpha + kx)]\}$$

$$\mu = 0 \cdot 20, \quad k = 0 \cdot 01 \text{ m}^{-1}$$

(*b*) Draw-in of the anchorages = 6 mm
(*c*) Concrete deformation
Average decrease of each strand ΔP is estimated from following formula

$$\Delta P = \Delta\sigma_p A_p$$

$$\Delta\sigma_p = \tfrac{1}{2}\alpha\sigma_{cpg} \frac{N-1}{N}$$

where $\alpha = E_s/E_{cm}$, N is number of strands in a section, and σ_{cpg} is concrete stress at centroid by prestress.
(*d*) Relaxation
Treated as though relaxation occurs immediately, $\Delta P_r = 5 \cdot 0\%$.

Time-dependent losses
Losses due to creep and shrinkage are estimated by calculating the strain of members.

E3.4. Design model
A two-dimensional frame model is used.

Acting forces moments, ar forces

Acting forces, moments and shear forces are computed by computer using an elastic frame analysis. The bending moment diagrams are shown in Figs E6–E11.

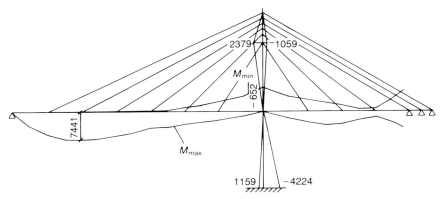

Fig. E7. Bending moments (kN m): live load

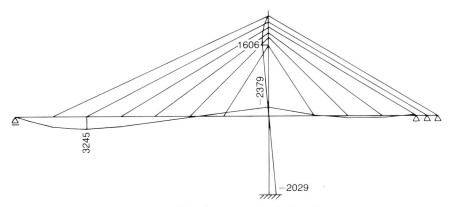

Fig. E8. Bending moments (kN m): creep and shrinkage

Table E4. Girder: acting design forces

	Section 1*		Section 3†	
	M: kN m	N: kN	M: kN m	N: kN
Dead load, G_1	26 163	−1054	−29 830	−6 890
Stay-cable tension, T	−25 200	−5119	28 695	−7 144
Live load, Q_1	7 296	232	−6 521	1 462
Earthquake, Q_2	536	1037	−417	2 876
$1{\cdot}35G_1 + 1{\cdot}0T + 1{\cdot}5Q_1 + 1{\cdot}5 \times 0{\cdot}3Q_2$‡	21 305	−5727	−21 545	−12 958

4.1.2

* Section 1: $M_{Sd} = 21\,305$ kN m, $N_{Sd} = -5727$ kN.
† Section 3: $M_{Sd} = -21\,545$ kN m, $N_{Sd} = -12\,958$ kN.
‡ Refer to section E1.3.4 for combination of actions. $\psi_0 = 0{\cdot}3$ (earthquake) chosen in connection with the Japanese specifications.[1]

Table E5. Pylon: acting design forces

	Section 4*		Section 5†	
	M: kN m	N: kN	M: kN m	N: kN
Dead load, G_1	−4661	−16 309	−16 517	−29 265
Stay-cable tension, T	3777	−10 255	14 887	−6 207
Live load, Q_1	−963	−2 410	−4 224	−3 020
Earthquake, Q_2	−4301	−376	−14 258	−385
$1{\cdot}35G_1 + 1{\cdot}0T + 1{\cdot}5Q_1 + 1{\cdot}5 \times 0{\cdot}3Q_2$‡	−5895	−36 056	−20 163	−50 418

4.1.2

* Section 4: $M_{Sd} = -5895$ kN m, $N_{Sd} = -36\,056$ kN.
† Section 5: $M_{Sd} = -20\,163$ kN m, $N_{Sd} = -50\,418$ kN.
‡ Refer to section E1.3.4 for combination of actions. $\psi_0 = 0{\cdot}3$ (earthquake) chosen in connection with the Japanese specifications.[1]

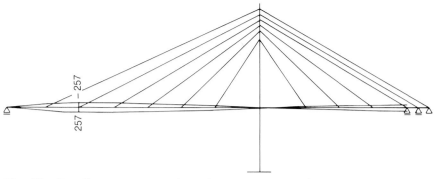

Fig. E9. Bending moments (kNm): temperature (for whole structure, ±15°C)

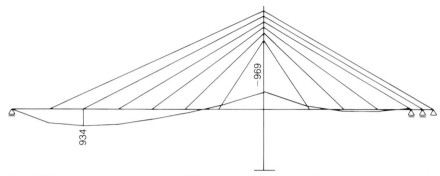

Fig. E10. Bending moments (kNm): temperature (for stay cables only, +10°C)

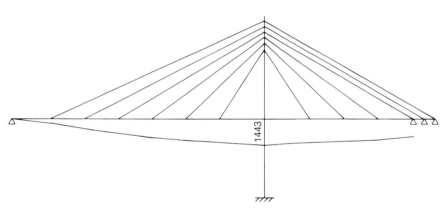

Fig. E11. Bending moments (kNm): temperature (for upper side of slab only, +5°C)

Ultimate limit state

E5.1. Moment calculation

E5.1.1. Acting design force

Tables E4 and E5 show the design forces acting at the critical sections.

E5.1.2. Calculation of resisting moment

  Girder section 1

See Figs E12 and E13.

Reinforcing steel

  A_s (14 bars of 22 mm dia.) = 54·19 cm^2

Prestressing steel

  A_{p1} (4 × 12 strands of 15·2 mm dia.) = 66·56 cm^2

  A_{p2} (4 × 12 strands of 15·2 mm dia.) = 66·56 cm^2

Figure E14 shows the ultimate state of the section for axial force $N = N_{Sd} = -5727$ kN.

Assumptions

Tensile strain is beyond yield: $\varepsilon_s > \varepsilon_y$.

Tensile strength is equal to $f_y \to \sigma_s = f_y$.

Neutral axis from top: $x = 147$ mm.

All tension

$$\sum F_t = 5419 \times 400 \times (1/1 \cdot 15) \times 1/1000$$
$$+ 6656 \times 1537 \times (1/1 \cdot 15) \times 1/1000$$
$$+ 6656 \times 1537 \times (1/1 \cdot 15) \times 1/1000$$
$$= 1885 + 8896 + 8896$$
$$= 19\,677 \text{ kN}$$

Concrete compressive force

$$F_c = 0 \cdot 80 \times 40 \times (1/1 \cdot 5) \times 0 \cdot 8 \times 147 \times 10\,150 \times 1/1000$$
$$= -25\,464 \text{ kN}$$

Resisting normal force

$$N_{Rd} = -25\,464 + 19\,677 = -5787 \approx N_{Sd} \quad \text{(OK)}$$

Resisting moment

$$M_{Rd} = 25\,464 \times 0 \cdot 088 + 1885 \times 1 \cdot 187 + 8896 \times 1 \cdot 053$$
$$+ 8896 \times 0 \cdot 853$$
$$= 21\,434 \text{ kN m}$$
$$\approx M_{Sd} = 21\,305 \text{ kN m} \quad \text{(OK)}$$

Girder section 3
See Figs E12 and E15.
Reinforcing steel

$$A_s \text{ (86 bars of 19 mm dia.)} = 246 \cdot 4 \text{ cm}^2$$

Prestressing steel

$$A_p \text{ (4} \times \text{12 strands of 15} \cdot \text{2 mm dia.)} = 66 \cdot 56 \text{ cm}^2$$

Assumptions

Tensile strain is beyond yield: $\varepsilon_s > \varepsilon_y$.

Tensile strength is equal to $f_y \to \sigma_s = f_y$.

Neutral axis from bottom: $x = 483$ mm.

Resisting moment

$$M_{Rd} = 22\,850 \text{ kN m}$$
$$> M_{Sd} = 21\,545 \text{ kN m} \quad \text{(OK)}$$

Pylon section 4
See Figs E16 and E17.
Reinforcing steel

$$A_s \text{ (7 bars of 29 mm dia.)} = 44 \cdot 97 \text{ cm}^2$$

Assumptions

Tensile strain is beyond yield: $\varepsilon_s = \varepsilon_y$.

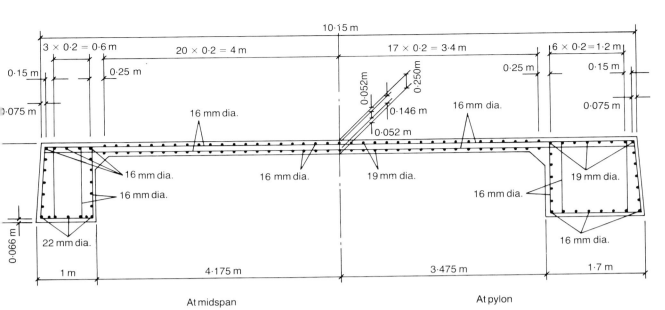

Fig. E12. Arrangement of reinforcing bars in girder sections

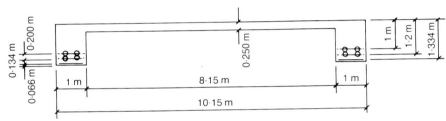

Fig. E13. Arrangement of tendons in girder section at midspan

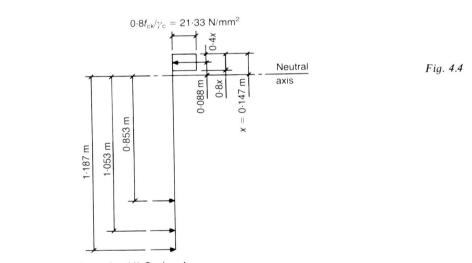

Fig. E14. Definitions for ULS check

Fig. 4.4

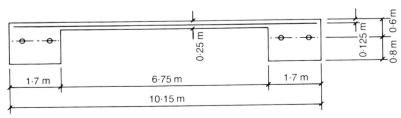

Fig. E15. Arrangement of tendons in girder section at pylon

Tensile strength is equal to $f_y \to \sigma_s = f_y$.

Neutral axis from bottom: $x = 764$ mm.

Resisting moment

$$M_{Rd} = 15\,360 \text{ kN m}$$
$$> M_{Sd} = 5895/2 = 2948 \text{ kN m} \text{ (OK)}$$

The horizontal deformation of the top of the pylon is 1·97 cm at live load.

As the second moment at section 4 is small, it is omitted in this example.

Pylon section 5
See Figs E16 and E18.
Reinforcing steel

$$A_s \text{ (25 bars of 29 mm dia.)} = 160 \cdot 6 \text{ cm}^2$$

Assumptions

Tensile strain is beyond yield: $\varepsilon_s > \varepsilon_y$.

Tensile strength is equal to $f_y \to \sigma_s = f_y$.

Neutral axis from top: $x = 515$ mm.

Resisting moment

$$M_{Rd} = 30\,188 \text{ kN m}$$
$$> M_{Sd} = 20\,163/2 = 10\,082 \text{ kN m} \text{ (OK)}$$

E5.1.3. Ductility check   4.2.4
The sections should satisfy the following condition

$$\rho_s + \rho_p \frac{f_{0 \cdot 1k}}{f_{yk}} \leqslant 0 \cdot 02$$

where

$$\rho_s = \frac{A_s}{bd_s}$$

$$\rho_p = \frac{A_p}{bd_p}$$

Girder section 1
See Fig. E13.

$$f_{0 \cdot 1k} = 1537 \text{ N/mm}^2$$
$$f_{yk} = 400 \text{ N/mm}^2$$

$$\rho_s + (\rho_{p1} + \rho_{p2}) \frac{f_{0 \cdot 1k}}{f_{yk}}$$
$$= \frac{5 \cdot 419 \times 10^{-3}}{10 \cdot 15 \times 1 \cdot 334} + \left\{ \frac{6 \cdot 66 \times 10^{-3}}{10 \cdot 15 \times 1 \cdot 20} + \frac{6 \cdot 66 \times 10^{-3}}{10 \cdot 15 \times 1 \cdot 00} \right\} \times \frac{1537}{400}$$
$$= 0 \cdot 005 < 0 \cdot 02 \text{ (OK)}$$

Girder section 3

$$\rho_s + \rho_p \frac{f_{0 \cdot 1k}}{f_{yk}} = \frac{246 \cdot 4 \times 10^{-4}}{3 \cdot 400 \times 1 \cdot 275} + \frac{66 \cdot 56 \times 10^{-4}}{3 \cdot 400 \times 0 \cdot 800} \times \frac{1537}{400}$$
$$= 0 \cdot 015 < 0 \cdot 02 \text{ (OK)}$$

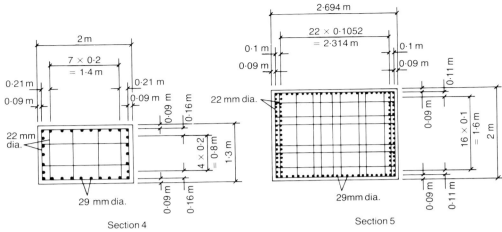

Fig. E16. Arrangement of reinforcing bars in pylon sections

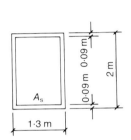

Fig. E17. Idealized pylon section at girder

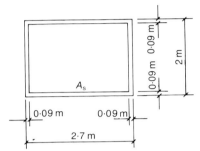

Fig. E18. Idealized pylon section at foundation

Pylon section 4

$$\rho_s = \frac{44 \cdot 97 \times 10^{-4}}{1 \cdot 300 \times 1 \cdot 910} = 0 \cdot 0018 < 0 \cdot 02 \quad (\text{OK})$$

Pylon section 5

$$\rho_s = \frac{160 \cdot 6 \times 10^{-4}}{2 \cdot 700 \times 1 \cdot 910} = 0 \cdot 0031 < 0 \cdot 02 \quad (\text{OK})$$

E5.2. Calculation of shear force

E5.2.1 Acting design force

Table E6 shows the acting forces for section 2.

The acting design forces are as follows   *4.1.2*

$$V_{Sd} = 1 \cdot 35G_1 + 1 \cdot 0T + 1 \cdot 5Q_1 + 1 \cdot 5 \times 0 \cdot 3Q_2$$

$$= -2925 \, \text{kN}$$

($\psi_0 = 0 \cdot 3$ (earthquake) chosen in connection with Japanese specifications.[1])

Table E6. *Section 2: acting forces*

	V: kN
Dead load, G_1	-2729
Stay-cable tension, T	1988
Live load, Q_1	-799
Earthquake, Q_2	-68

E5.2.2. Checks
 Upper limit of resistant shear force   *4.4.2*
The following condition should be satisfied

$$V_{Sd} \leqslant V_{Rd} = V_{Rd2} + A_p \sigma_{p0} \sin \alpha_p$$
$$V_{Rd2} = 0 \cdot 30 (f_{ck}/\gamma_c) b_w d$$
$$= 0 \cdot 30 \times (40/1 \cdot 5) \times 3250 \times 1334/1000$$
$$= 34\,684 \text{ kN}$$

The section satisfies the condition

$$V_{Sd} = 2925 < V_{Rd2} = 34\,684 \text{ kN}$$

Stirrups
The following condition should be satisfied

$$V_{Sd} \leqslant V_{wd} + V_{cd} + A_p \sigma_{p0} \sin \alpha_p$$
$$\alpha_p = 0 \text{ gives } A_p \sigma_{p0} \sin \alpha_p = 0$$

$$V_{cd} = 2 \cdot 5 \tau_{Rd} b_w d \left\{ 1 + \frac{M_o}{M_{Sdu}} \right\}$$

$$= 2 \cdot 5 \times 0 \cdot 42 \times 3250 \times 1334 \times \left\{ 1 + \frac{M_o}{M_{Sdu}} \right\}$$

$$= 4552 \times \left\{ 1 + \frac{M_o}{M_{Sdu}} \right\} \text{ kN}$$

$$M_{Sdu} = -9266 \text{ kN m}$$

$$M_o = \frac{I}{y_u} \left\{ \frac{N}{A} + \frac{M}{I} y_u \right\}$$

The acting forces are shown in Table E7.

$$A = 6 \cdot 249 \text{ m}^2$$
$$I = 1 \cdot 159 \text{ m}^4$$
$$y_u = 0 \cdot 5361 \text{ m}$$

$$M_o = \frac{1 \cdot 159}{0 \cdot 5361} \left\{ \frac{18\,447}{6 \cdot 249} - \frac{3011}{1 \cdot 159} \times 0 \cdot 5361 \right\}$$
$$= -3371 \text{ kN m}$$

$$1 + \frac{M_o}{M_{Sdu}} = 1 + \frac{-3371}{-9266} = 1 \cdot 364 < 2 \cdot 0$$

$$V_{cd} = 4552 \times 1 \cdot 364 = 6209 \text{ kN}$$

Resistant shear force by stirrups

$$V_{wd} = 0 \cdot 9d \, \frac{A_{sw}}{s} f_{ywd}$$

Table E7. Section 2: acting forces

	M: kN m	N: kN
Dead load + stay-cable tension	-359	$-14\,035$
Creep and shrinkage	-2188	$1\,066$
Prestress $\times$ 0·9	-464	$-5\,478$
Total	-3011	$-18\,447$

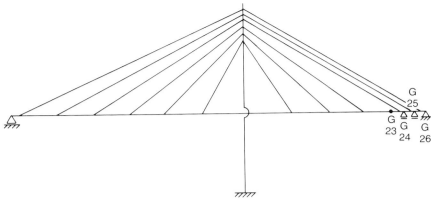

Fig. E19. Design model for computation: node numbers indicated are the numbers used for computer analysis

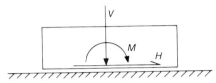

Fig. E20. Free-body diagram for abutment

Stirrups 16 mm dia., $s = 300$ mm

$$A_{sw} = 198\cdot6 \times 8 = 1598\cdot8 \text{ mm}^2$$

$$V_{wd} = 0\cdot9 \times 1334 \times \frac{1598\cdot8}{300} \times \frac{400}{1\cdot15} \times \frac{1}{1000}$$

$$= 2226 \text{ kN}$$

Therefore

$$V_{Sd} = 2925 < V_{wd} + V_{cd} = 2226 + 6209 = 8435 \quad \text{(OK)}$$

Detailing of shear reinforcement

$$\rho_w = \frac{A_{sw}}{sb_w \sin \alpha} = \frac{1598\cdot8}{300 \times 3250}$$

$$= 0\cdot00164 > 0\cdot0015 \qquad \text{(OK)}$$

E5.3. Equilibrium of abutment A$_2$

4.7

E5.3.1. General

The check consists of proving that, with regard to sliding, over-turning and lifting at the supports

(a) the permanent stabilizing action G_1
(b) the permanent non-stabilizing actions G_2 and
(c) the variable non-stabilizing actions Q

(the actions being taken at their absolute value) satisfy the following condition

$$S(0\cdot9G_1 - 1\cdot1G_2 - 1\cdot5Q_1 - 1\cdot5\Sigma\psi_0 Q_2) \geqslant 0 \qquad \text{(E1)}$$

where Q_1 is basic variable action and Q_2 is other variable action (earthquake action). The value of ψ_0 is assumed to be $0\cdot3$.[1]

The design model for computation is shown in Fig. E19. At each support the three actions considered are as shown in Fig. E20. The

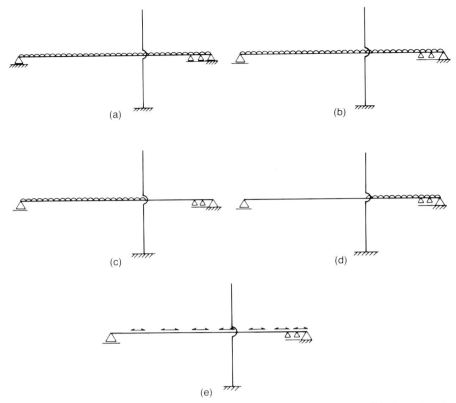

Fig. E21. (a) Dead load (G_1) plus stay-cable adjustment; (b) live load (Q_1) (full span); (c) live load (Q_1) (part span); (d) live load (Q_1) (part span); (e) earthquake load (Q_2)

effect of these are sliding due to H, overturning due to M and settling (vertical instability) due to V. Therefore in order that the structure be stable, each of these actions must satisfy equation (E1).

Equation (E1) is applied below for various loading cases.

E5.3.2. Loading cases
Consider the loading cases shown in Fig. E21. Details of abutment A_2 are shown in Fig. E22. The support reactions $(\downarrow V, \widetilde{M}, \vec{H})$ at the abutment for each of the five cases are shown in Table E8.

E5.3.3. Stability check
Calculation of stabilizing actions
The stabilizing actions for the abutment are assumed to be the reaction forces working on the abutment face due to the soil. If these resisting forces are greater than the actions due to the different loadings, then the structure is said to be safe. The normal design bearing capacity of 600 kN/m² is assumed for a conservative design.

Table E8. Nodal loads at abutment A_2 for the five loading cases defined in Fig. E21

Loading case	Node 23			Node 24	Node 25	Node 26	
	V_1: kN	H_1: kN	M_1: kNm	V_2: kN	V_3: kN	V_4: kN	H_4: kN
(a)	640	8000	1090	−140	−2360	−1580	—
(b)	−320	1060	1390	950	−970	0	−230
(c)	480	1280	−4420	−2800	2270	−630	−170
(d)	−800	−220	5810	3750	−3240	630	−60
(e)	200	4800	−1780	1140	−940	220	−5430

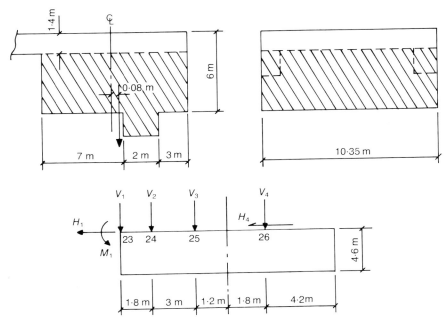

Fig. E22. Details of abutment A_2

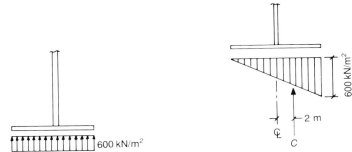

Fig. E23. Assumption for maximum vertical force

Fig. E24. Assumption for maximum moment

(a) *To calculate maximum vertical resisting force, V*
See Fig. E23.

$$V = (12 \times 10 \cdot 35) \times 600 \text{ kN}$$

$$= 74\,520 \text{ kN}$$

(b) *To calculate maximum bending resistance, M*
See Fig. E24.

$$C = (12 \times 10 \cdot 35) \times 600/2 \text{ kN}$$

$$= 37\,260 \text{ kN}$$

$$M = 2 \times 37\,260 \text{ kN m}$$

$$= 74\,520 \text{ kN m}$$

(c) *To calculate the maximum horizontal reaction from the soil*
See Fig. E25.

$$P_{EA} = (\gamma x K_{EA} - \tau_c K_{EA}^{1/2} + q' K_{EA})$$

where

$$K_{EA} = \cos^2(\phi - Q_0 - Q) \bigg/ \bigg[\cos Q_0 \cos^2 Q \cos (Q + Q_0 + \delta)$$

$$\times \left(1 + \left\{ \frac{\sin(\phi + \delta)\sin(\phi - \alpha - Q_0)}{\cos(Q + Q_0 + \delta)\cos(Q - \alpha)} \right\}^{1/2} \right)^2 \bigg]$$

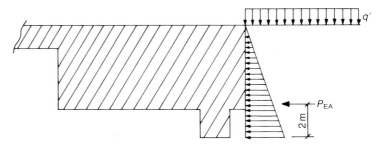

Fig. E25. Assumption for maximum horizontal force

γ (self-weight of soil) $= 19$ kN/m^2, C (cohesive force) $= 0$, q' (external force) $= 0$, $\phi = 30°$, $\alpha = 0$, $Q = 0$ and $Q_0 = \tan^{-1} 0.23 = 12.95°$.

$$K_{EA} = \cos^2(30° - 12.95°) \Big/ \Bigg[\cos 12.95° \times 1^2 \times \cos 12.95°$$

$$\times \left(1 + \left\{ \frac{\sin 30° \times \sin(30° - 12.95°)}{\cos 12.95° \times 1} \right\}^{1/2} \right)^2 \Bigg]$$

$$= 0.5$$

$$P_{EA} = \tfrac{1}{2} r H^2 K_{EA} L$$

$$= \tfrac{1}{2} \times 19 \times 7.5^2 \times 0.5 \times 10.35 = 2760 \text{ kN}$$

Weight of abutment $= 17\,150$ kN
Therefore

$$\text{total horizontal resistance} = 2760 + 0.6 \times 17\,150 \text{ kN}$$

$$= 13\,050 \text{ kN}$$

Application of equation (E1)

In calculating the values of G_1, G_2, Q_1 and Q_2, the resultants of all actions are considered around the centre-line of the base.

In the following analysis, in calculating the value Q_1, nodal loads are assumed based on loading cases (b), (c) and (d), but the following example calculation is shown only for case (d), as this seems to be the critical case.

Table E9. Girder: acting design forces

	Section 1		Section 3		
	M: kN m	N: kN	M: kN m	N: kN	V: kN
Dead load, G_1	26 163	−1 054	−29 830	−6 890	−3056
Stay-cable tension, T	−25 200	−5 119	28 695	−7 144	1988
Creep and shrinkage, G_2	3 036	1 430	−2 379	1 049	−110
Prestress, P	−1 617	−14 241	−1 000	−6 148	−310
Live load, Q_1	7 296	232	−6 521	1 462	−867
Temperature, Q_2	1 127	223	−975	188	−76
Earthquake, Q_3	536	1 037	−417	2 876	−68
Frequent combinations					
$\sum G + T + P + 0.57 Q_1$	6 541	−18 851	−8 230	−18 300	−1982
$\sum G + T + P + 0.57 Q_2$	3 025	−18 857	−5 069	−19 026	−1531
Infrequent combinations					
$\sum G + T + P + Q_1 + 0.57(Q_2 + Q_3)$	10 627	−18 034	−11 827	−15 925	−2437
$\sum G + T + P + Q_2 + 0.57(Q_1 + Q_3)$	7 974	−18 038	−9 442	−16 472	−2097
$\sum G + T + P + Q_3 + 0.57(Q_1 + Q_2)$	7 720	−17 688	−9 202	−15 317	−2094

Table

Table

Check for overturning

$G_1 = 74\,520 \text{ kN m}$

$G_2 = 17\,150 \times 0 \cdot 08 - 8000 \times 4 \cdot 6 + 140 \times 4 \cdot 2 + 2360 \times 1 \cdot 2$
$\qquad - 1090 - 1580 \times 1 \cdot 8 - 640 \times 6$
$\quad = -39\,782 \text{ kN m}$

$Q_1 = 5810 + 3750 \times 4 \cdot 2 - 220 \times 4 \cdot 6 - 800 \times 6 - 3240 \times 1 \cdot 2$
$\qquad - 630 \times 1 \cdot 8 - 60 \times 4 \cdot 6$
$\quad = 10\,450 \text{ kN m}$

$Q_2 = (5430 - 4800) \times 4 \cdot 6 + 220 \times 1 \cdot 8 + 940 \times 1 \cdot 2 + 1780$
$\qquad - 200 \times 6 - 1140 \times 4 \cdot 2$
$\quad = 214 \text{ kN m}$

Therefore

$S = 0 \cdot 9 \times 74\,520 - 1 \cdot 1 \times 39\,782 - 1 \cdot 5 \times 10\,450 - 0 \cdot 45 \times 214$
$\quad = 7536 \cdot 5 > 0$

(OK for overturning)

Check for horizontal stability

$G_1 = 2760 + 0 \cdot 6 \times 17\,150 = 13\,050 \text{ kN}$

$G_2 = 8000 \text{ kN}$

$Q_1 = -220 - 60 = -280 \text{ kN}$

$Q_2 = 5430 - 4800 = 630 \text{ kN}$

$S = 0 \cdot 9 \times 13\,050 - 1 \cdot 1 \times 8000 - 1 \cdot 5 \times 280 - 0 \cdot 45 \times 630$
$\quad = 2242 > 0$

(OK for sliding)

Check for vertical stability

$G_1 = 74\,520 \text{ kN}$

$G_2 = -2360 - 1580 - 140 + 640 + 17\,150 = 13\,710 \text{ kN}$

$Q_1 = 3750 + 630 - 800 - 3240 = 340 \text{ kN}$

$Q_2 = 200 + 1140 - 940 + 220 = 620 \text{ kN}$

$S = 0 \cdot 9 \times 74\,520 - 1 \cdot 1 \times 13\,710 - 1 \cdot 5 \times 340 - 1 \cdot 5 \times 0 \cdot 3 \times 620$
$\quad = 51\,198 > 0$

(OK)

Hence abutment A_2 is stable.

E6. Serviceability limit state

E6.1. Girder and pylon

E6.1.1. Acting design force

The acting design forces at the critical sections of the girder are shown in Table E9.

In accordance with the Japanese rules,[1] the combination values have been simplified: $\psi_2 = 0$ for Q_1, Q_2 and Q_3, and $\psi_1 = 0 \cdot 57$ for live load, temperature and earthquake.

The live load is in accordance with Table 5.1 of the recommendations, where no values for temperature and earthquake are given. However, MC78 (Volume I, Appendix III) suggests, for temperature,

$\psi_1 = 0.5$ and $\psi_2 = 0.3$; and suggests that, for serviceability limit state, earthquake action may be considered to be negligible.

The design forces acting at the critical sections of the pylon are shown in Table E10. Values of N are calculated in the same state of M.

E6.1.2. Concrete in compression   5.3.1
The compression stress of concrete is checked under infrequent combinations of actions.

Girder section 1

$$M = 10\,627 \text{ kN m}, \quad N = -18\,034 \text{ kN}$$

Stress at top fibre

$$\sigma_{cc} = 15.2 \text{ N/mm}^2 < 0.5f_{ck} = 20 \text{ N/mm}^2 \quad \text{(OK)}$$

Girder section 3

$$M = -11\,827 \text{ kN m}, \quad N = -15\,925 \text{ kN}$$

Stress at bottom fibre

$$\sigma_{cc} = 13.9 \text{ N/mm}^2 < 0.5f_{ck} = 20 \text{ N/mm}^2 \quad \text{(OK)}$$

Pylon section 4

$$M = -5536/2 = -2768 \text{ kN m}$$

$$N = -25\,525/2 = -12\,763 \text{ kN}$$

Stress at bottom fibre

$$\sigma_{cc} = 7.9 \text{ N/mm}^2 < 0.5f_{ck} = 20 \text{ N/mm}^2 \quad \text{(OK)}$$

Pylon section 5

$$M = -19\,386/2 = -9693 \text{ kN m}$$

$$N = -35\,623/2 = -17\,812 \text{ kN}$$

Stress at bottom fibre

$$\sigma_{cc} = 8.7 \text{ N/mm}^2 < 0.5f_{ck} = 20 \text{ N/mm}^2 \quad \text{(OK)}$$

Table E10. Pylon: acting design forces

	Section 4		Section 5		
	M: kN m	N: kN	M: kN m	N: kN	
Dead load, G_1	− 4661	− 16 309	− 16 517	− 29 265	
Stay-cable tension, T	3777	− 10 255	14 887	− 6 207	
Creep and shrinkage, G_2	− 233	1 440	− 2 029	962	
Prestress, P	698	1 259	1 558	903	
Live load, Q_1	− 963	− 2 410	− 4 224	− 3 020	
Temperature, Q_2	− 469	158	− 1 086	158	
Earthquake Q_3	− 4301	− 376	− 14 258	− 385	
Frequent combinations					Table
$\sum G + T + P + 0.57Q_1$	− 968	− 25 239	− 4 509	− 35 328	
$\sum G + T + P + 0.57Q_2$	− 686	− 23 775	− 2 720	− 33 517	
Infrequent combinations					Table
$\sum G + T + P + Q_1 + 0.57(Q_2 + Q_3)$	− 4101	− 26 399	− 10 847	− 36 756	
$\sum G + T + P + Q_2 + 0.57(Q_1 + Q_3)$	− 2950	− 25 295	− 13 722	− 35 390	
$\sum G + T + P + Q_3 + 0.57(Q_1 + Q_2)$	− 5536	− 25 525	− 19 386	− 35 623	

E6.1.3. Crack control   5.3.2
Crack width is checked under frequent combinations of actions.   *Table 5.1*

Girder section 1

$$\sigma_{ct} = \frac{N}{A} + \frac{M}{W} = \frac{-18\,851}{4\cdot811} + \frac{6541}{0\cdot8961}$$

$$= 3381\cdot3 \text{ kN/m}^2$$

$$= 3\cdot38 \text{ N/mm}^2 > 0\cdot75 f_{ctk} = 1\cdot79 \text{ N/mm}^2 \rightarrow \text{cracked}$$

This section is considered cracked. Assuming that the concrete does not provide tensile resistance, the stress in the concrete at the top fibre is

$$\sigma_{cc} = 7\cdot4 \text{ N/mm}^2$$

and in the reinforcement steel is

$$\sigma_s = 79\cdot2 \text{ N/mm}^2$$

Crack width

$$w_k = s\left(1\cdot5 + \frac{3\cdot5c}{s}\right)\frac{\sigma_s}{E_s}\left(1 - \left\{\frac{M_r}{M}\right\}^2\right)$$

Cracking moment

$$M_r = \left\{0\cdot75 f_{ctk} - \frac{N}{A}\right\}W$$

$$= \left\{1790 + \frac{18\,851}{4\cdot811}\right\} \times 0\cdot8961 = 5115\cdot3 \text{ kN m}$$

$$s = 200 \text{ mm}, \quad c = 58 \text{ mm}, \quad E_s = 200 \text{ kN/mm}^2$$

$$w_k = 200\left(1\cdot5 + \frac{3\cdot5 \times 58}{200}\right) \times \frac{79\cdot2}{200 \times 10^3} \times \left(1 - \left\{\frac{5115}{6541}\right\}^2\right)$$

$$= 0\cdot077 \text{ mm} < w_{req} = 0\cdot1 \text{ mm} \quad (\text{OK})$$

Girder section 3

$$M = -8230 \text{ kN m}, \quad N = -18\,300 \text{ kN}$$

$$\sigma_{ct} = \frac{-18\,300}{6\cdot421} + \frac{8230}{1\cdot7898} \text{ kN/m}^2$$

$$= 1\cdot75 \text{ N/mm}^2 < 0\cdot75 f_{ctk} = 1\cdot79 \text{ N/mm}^2 \rightarrow \text{uncracked}$$

Pylon section 4

$$M = -968/2 = -484 \text{ kN m}$$

$$N = -25\,239/2 = -12\,620 \text{ kN}$$

$$\sigma_{ct} = \frac{-12\,620}{1\cdot30 \times 2\cdot00} + \frac{484}{1\cdot30 \times 2\cdot00^2 \times 1/6}$$

$$= -4854 + 558$$

$$= -4296 \text{ kN/m}^2 = -4\cdot30 \text{ N/mm}^2 \rightarrow \text{uncracked}$$

Pylon section 5

$$M = -4509/2 = -2255 \text{ kN m}$$

$$N = -35\,328/2 = -17\,664 \text{ kN}$$

$$\sigma_u = \frac{-17\,664}{2\cdot70 \times 2\cdot00} + \frac{2255}{2\cdot70 \times 2\cdot00^2 \times 1/6}$$

$$= -3271 + 1253$$

$$= -2018 \text{ kN/m}^2 = -2\cdot02 \text{ N/mm}^2 \rightarrow \text{uncracked}$$

E6.1.4. Concrete in tension
Girder section 3
This section remains in an uncracked state.

Check of the principal diagonal tensile stress at centroid

$$M = -8230 \text{ kN m}, \quad N = -18\,300 \text{ kN}, \quad V = 1982 \text{ kN}$$

$$\sigma_1 = \frac{\sigma_x}{2} - \tfrac{1}{2}(\sigma_x^2 + 4\tau^2)^{1/2}$$

$$\sigma_x = \frac{N}{A} = \frac{-18\,300 \times 10^3}{6\cdot421 \times 10^6} = -2\cdot850 \text{ N/mm}^2$$

$$\tau = \frac{VS}{b_w I}$$

$$= \frac{1982 \times 1\cdot240}{1\cdot70 \times 2 \times 1\cdot196} = 604 \text{ kN/m}^2 = 0\cdot604 \text{ N/mm}^2$$

Table E11. Cables: acting design forces

	N: kN			
	Cable C1	Cable C3	Cable C6	Cable C12
Dead load + stay-cable tension, $G_1 + G_2$	4314	3391	2641	3943
Creep and shrinkage, G_3	−642	−186	−17	−305
Prestress, P	−107	−309	−39	−230
Live load, Q_1				
Maximum	82	515	420	401
Minimum	−71	−5	−419	−55
Temperature, Q_2	45	8	7	18
Earthquake, Q_3	28	14	57	99
Frequent				
$\sum G + P + 0\cdot57Q_1$	3612	3190	2824	3637
$\sum G + P + 0\cdot57Q_2$	3591	2901	2589	3418
Infrequent				
$\sum G + P + Q_1 + 0\cdot57(Q_2 + Q_3)$	3689	3424	3041	3876
$\sum G + P + Q_2 + 0\cdot57(Q_1 + Q_3)$	3673	3206	2864	3711
$\sum G + P + Q_3 + 0\cdot57(Q_1 + Q_2)$	3665	3208	2885	3746

Table E12. Cable stresses

	Cable C1	Cable C3	Cable C6	Cable C12
Sectional area of stay cables: mm²	7212	5548	4161	6380
Maximum stress: N/mm²	598	617	731	618
Variable stress: N/mm²	21	94	202	71
Allowable stress: N/mm²	0·4 × 1862 = 745			

Therefore

$$\sigma_l = \frac{-2 \cdot 850}{2} + \tfrac{1}{2}(2 \cdot 850^2 + 4 \times 0 \cdot 604^2)^{1/2}$$

$$= 0 \cdot 123 \ \text{N/mm}^2 < 0 \cdot 75 f_{ck} = 1 \cdot 79 \ \text{N/mm}^2 \quad (\text{OK})$$

E6.1.5. Minimum reinforcement   *5.5.6*
  Girder section 1

$$s = 200 \ \text{mm}, \ h_{ef} = 200 \ \text{mm}, \ h_t = 912 \ \text{mm}$$

$$\frac{h_{ef}}{h_t} = \frac{200}{912} = 0 \cdot 22 \ \text{gives} \ \rho_{r\,min} = 0 \cdot 57\%$$

$$A_{c\,ef} = 200 \times 2000 = 400\,000 \ \text{mm}^2$$

$$A_{s\,min} = A_{c\,ef} \times \rho_{r\,min} = 2280 \ \text{mm}^2$$

$$A_s = 5419 \ \text{mm}^2 > A_{s\,min} = 2280 \ \text{mm}^2 \quad (\text{OK})$$

Girder section 3

$$s = 200 \ \text{mm}$$

$$h_{ef}/h_t \approx 0 \ \text{gives} \ \rho_{r\,min} = 0 \cdot 75\%$$

$$A_{c\,ef} = 1737\,500 \ \text{mm}^2$$

$$A_{s\,min} = 1737\,500 \times 0 \cdot 0075 = 13\,031 \ \text{mm}^2$$

$$A_s = 20\,600 \ \text{mm}^2 > A_{s\,min} = 13\,031 \ \text{mm}^2 \quad (\text{OK})$$

E6.2. Cables
Acting design forces are shown in Table E11. (For values of ψ_1 and ψ_2, see section E6.1.1.)

According to the Japan Road Association's *Specifications for road bridges*,[1] the allowable stress of the stay cable is $0 \cdot 4 f_{tk}$, where f_{tk} is the tensile stength of the strands. See Table E12.

According to other codes (e.g. DIN 4227), both the maximum stress and the variable stress have to be checked.

erence

1. Japan Road Association. *Specifications for road bridges*. 1978.

Example F

Rivoli Bianchi Bridge, Italy: single-span beam for double-track railway bridge

Design for fatigue

Example prepared by R. Calzona (Rome)

References to *FIP recommendations: Practical design of reinforced and prestressed concrete structures (based on the CEB–FIP model code (MC78))* are given in the right-hand margin

. Introduction:
igue

Fatigue is the decay of mechanical characteristics under cyclic loads. The decay depends mainly on the amplitude of the stress range and the number of cycles.

For reinforcing bars and prestressing wires or strands, the main effect of fatigue is the reduction of strength. However, this effect becomes significant only when the concrete is cracked.

Fatigue in concrete leads to a reduction of compressive, tensile and bond strengths, and to an increase of deformability.

Figure F1 shows how the stress–strain diagram for uniaxial load changes as the number of cycles, n, increases.

The effects of fatigue on structural elements can be summarized as follows

(a) a reduction of safety due to decay of the strength of the concrete and steel
(b) a reduction of cracking resistance due to decay of the tensile strength of the concrete
(c) an acceleration in crack development due to loss of bond
(d) an increase of deformations due to an increase in concrete strains and crack development
(e) a reduction of cracking moment in prestressed concrete structures due to an increase in losses of prestress
(f) cracks and early ruptures where heavy concentrated loads are applied.

A railway bridge is a typical structure affected by cyclic loads and therefore by fatigue effects. The example concerns a railway bridge (Figs F2 and F3) which serves a new double-track railway line, Udine–Tarvisio, in northern Italy. The bridge was designed according to the Italian code for reinforced and prestressed concrete structures and to further design requirements of the Italian Railway Administration, as follows

(a) no concrete tensile stresses under dead and maximum live load
(b) maximum deflection under maximum live load $\delta \leqslant L/2000$
(c) allowable stress for reinforcing steel $\sigma_s \leqslant 180 \text{ N/mm}^2$.

These last requirements involve an implicit fatigue check. In fact, the calculations presented here (in accordance with the FIP recommendations) show that fatigue effects are irrelevant.

Special emphasis is also given to additional calculation procedures and structural detailing which provided further reliability against fatigue (section F7).

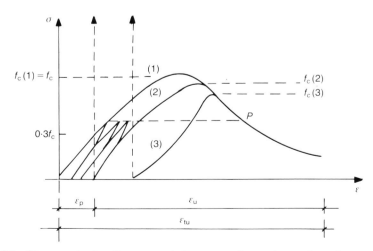

Fig. F1. Stress–strain diagram: influence of number of cycles, n, with
$n_3 > n_2 > n_1$

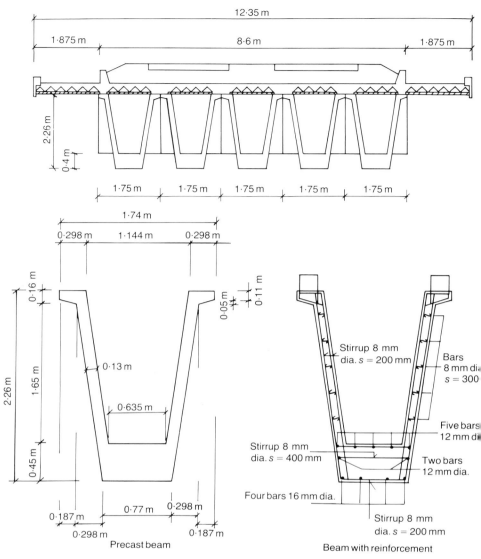

Fig. F2. Cross-sections (including reinforcement)

F2. Design information

F2.1. Structural summary

System

Single span $L = 27 \cdot 50$ m of multispan bridge of 35 times 30 m (total length 1·050 km).

Cross-section

Five precast V beams, spacing 1·75 m, connected by 0·24 m thick in situ slab and four transverse girders.

Prestressing

Straight strands applied on single-span precast girder 1 day after steam curing. Slab and transverse girders concreted after 42 days.

F2.2. Materials

Concrete

    precast beam   C50

    in situ slab   C35

Reinforcing steel: $f_{yk} = 440$ N/mm^2

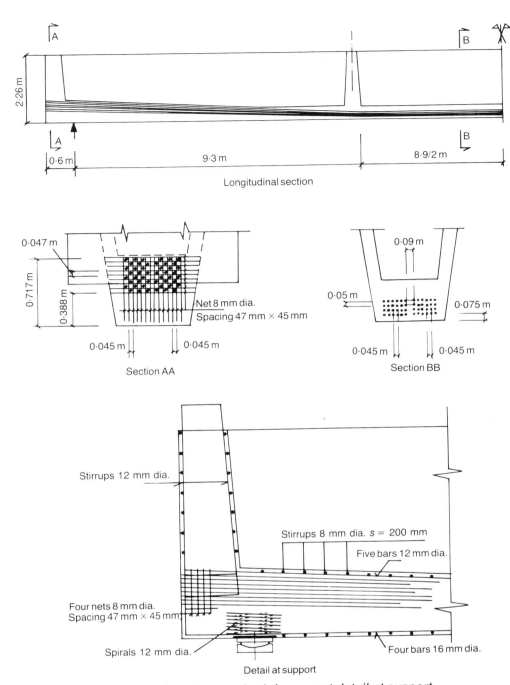

Fig. F3. *Arrangement of tendons, and reinforcement detail at support*

Prestressing steel (strands)

S1600/1800

48 strands

$A_p = 48 \times 139 = 6672 \text{ mm}^2$

F2.3. Loading conditions

Girder, slab $\quad \gamma = 25 \text{ kN/m}^3$

Ballast $\qquad \gamma = 18 \text{ kN/m}^3$

Live loads see section F3.2.2 $\quad \big\}$ Requirements of the Italian
Dynamic coefficient $\quad \Phi = 1 \cdot 167 \big\}$ Railway Administration

F2.4. Serviceability conditions

Relative humidity 75%
Concrete cover 30 mm
Permanent loading fully prestressed ⎫ Requirements of
Under maximum loading fully prestressed ⎬ the Italian Railway
Deflection limit $(1/2000)L$ ⎭ Administration
Crack limit —

F3. Basic data

F3.1. Materials

Concrete 2.1
See Table F1.

Reinforcing steel (high bond) 2.2

Strength: $f_{yk} = 440$ N/mm^2 2.2.2

E-modulus: $E_s = 200$ kN/mm^2 2.2.5

Fatigue strength: $\Delta f_{sk} = 150$ N/mm^2 2.2.9

Table F1. Concrete data

	Precast beam		Slab, 28 days	
	24 hours	28 days		
Compressive strength, f_{ck}: N/mm^2	38	50	35	Fig. 2.
Tensile strength, f_{ct}: N/mm^2	3.3	4.0	3.1	Fig. 2.
E-modulus, E_{cm}: kN/mm^2	34.5	37	33.5	Fig. 2.
Shrinkage, $\varepsilon_{cs}(t, t_0) \times 10^3$	0.26	0.23	0.23	Table
Creep, $\varphi(t, t_0)$	2.7	2.2	2.7	Table

Table F2. Distance of reinforcement from bottom

	In midspan	At support
Lowest strands	75 mm	388 mm
Reinforcing steel	30 mm	30 mm

Table F3. Construction programme

	Time
Casting girder	0
Tensioning	24 hours
Placed in final position	28 days
Concreting of slab	42 days
Surfacing	90 days

Table F4. Losses due to creep

Period: days	$\Delta\varphi/\varphi_\infty$	σ_{cp}: N/mm^2	$\Delta\sigma_p$: N/mm^2	
0–56	45%	16·3	107	
56–90	8%	11·7	13	Fig. 2.
90–∞	47%	7·5	51	
Total	—	—	171	

Prestressing steel (strands) 2.3

Characteristic strength: $f_{0.1k} = 1600 \text{ N/mm}^2$ 2.3.2

Tensile strength: $f_{tk} = 1800 \text{ N/mm}^2$ 2.3.2

Relaxation (final values) 5% Fig. 2.8

E-modulus: $E_s = 200 \text{ kN/mm}^2$ 2.3.5

Fatigue strength: $\Delta f_{sk} = 200 \text{ N/mm}^2$ 2.3.9

F3.2. Loadings
F3.2.1. Dead load 4.1.1
For each beam (Figs F2 and F3)

Girder: $g_0 = 0.932 \times 25 = 23.03 \text{ kN/m}$

Slab: $g_1 = 0.24 \times 12.35 \times 25/5 = 14.82 \text{ kN/m}$

Ballast: $g_2 = 0.70 \times 8.60 \times 18/5 = 21.70 \text{ kN/m}$

Transverse
girders, etc.

$$\text{Total } g = \frac{2.55 \text{ kN/m}}{62.10 \text{ kN/m}}$$

F3.2.2. Live load 4.1.1
For each track

Equivalent flexional loading: $q_f = 132\Phi = 154 \text{ kN/m}$

Equivalent shear loading: $q_s = 147\Phi = 172 \text{ kN/m}$

F3.3. Position of reinforcement
See Fig. F3 and Table F2.

4. Prestressing

F4.1. At the moment of tensioning 3.2.1

$$\sigma_{pi} \leqslant \begin{cases} 0.90 \times 1600 = 1440 \text{ N/mm}^2 \\ 0.80 \times 1800 = 1440 \text{ N/mm}^2 \end{cases}$$

$$P_i = 6.672 \times 1400 = 9340 \text{ kN}$$

F4.2. Initial prestress after transfer 3.2.1

$$\sigma_{p0} \leqslant \begin{cases} 0.85 \times 1600 = 1360 \text{ N/mm}^2 \\ 0.75 \times 1800 = 1350 \text{ N/mm}^2 \end{cases}$$

F4.3. Immediate losses (in midspan) 3.3.2
For instantaneous concrete deformation

$$\Delta P = \alpha \sigma_{cpi} A_p = 5.8 \times 20.2 \times 6.672 = 784 \text{ kN}$$

$$P_0 = P_i - \Delta P = 8556 \text{ kN}$$

$$\sigma_{p0} = P_0/A_p = 1282 < 1350 \text{ N/mm}^2$$ 3.2.1

F4.4. Estimation of time-dependent losses 3.3.3
Construction programme
See Table F3.

Losses due to creep (in midspan) 3.3.3
Creep: $\varphi_\infty = 2.7$.
σ_{cp} from section F6.3.

$$\Delta\sigma_p = \alpha\Delta\varphi\sigma_{cp}$$

See Table F4.

Loss of prestress 13%.

3.3.3
> *Losses due to shrinkage*
>
> $\Delta\sigma_p = 0.26 \times 200 = 52 \text{ N/mm}^2$

Loss of prestress 4%.

3.3.3
> *Losses due to relaxation*

Estimated total losses: $\Delta\sigma_p = 244 \text{ N/mm}^2$.

> $\sigma_p/f_{tk} = (1283 - 0.3 \times 244)/1800 = 0.67$

Fig. 2
Loss of prestress 5%.
Calculated total losses: $\Delta\sigma_p = 241 \text{ N/mm}^2$.

3.3.3
> *Total losses*
>
> $L(\%) = 13\% + 4\% + 5\% = 22\%$

Total obtained by superposition may be divided by

$$1 - 5.4 \times \frac{-17}{1283} \times \left\{1 + \frac{2.7}{2}\right\} = 1.17$$

$$L(\%) = 22\%/1.17 = 18.8\%$$

Fig. 4
Before 56 days   6.6%
After   56 days 12.2%

3.4.2
F4.5. Prestressing forces in midspan
$P_0 = 8556 \text{ kN}$
$P_{56} = (1 - 0.066)P_0 = 7980 \text{ kN}$
$P_\infty = (1 - 0.188)P_0 = 6947 \text{ kN}$

F5. Ultimate limit state design

4
4.2.2
F5.1. Principle
The static method of the theory of plasticity is used: the load distribution in the transverse direction at ultimate limit state is supposed constant, and the moment distribution in the longitudinal direction is given by Fig. F4.

1.2
Condition to be fulfilled

$$M_{Sd} \leqslant M_{Rd}$$

with

4.1.2
4.1.3
Figs
2.6,
$$M_{Sd} = M(1.35g; 1.5q)$$
$$M_{Rd} = M(0.8f_{ck}/1.5; f_y/1.15; f_{0.1k}/1.15)$$

Table F5. Reinforcement tensile forces

	d_s: m	A_s: mm²	f_{sd}: N/mm²	F_s: kN
48 strands of 0·6 in dia.	2·36	6672	1391	9281
Four bars of 16 mm dia.	2·47	803	382	307
Five bars of 12 mm dia.	2·08	565	382	216
Total	—	—	—	9804

Table F6. Reinforcement compressive forces

	d_s: m	A_s: mm²	f_{sd}: N/mm²	F_{sc}: kN
Bars 10 mm dia., $s = 40$	0·03	484	382	185

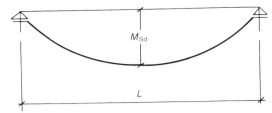

Fig. F4. Moment distribution in longitudinal direction

Acting moment at midspan, M_{Sd}

Dead load (section F3.2.1): $g = 62 \cdot 10$ kN/m.

$$M_{gd} = 1 \cdot 35 g L^2 / 8 = 7925 \text{ kN m}$$

Live load (section F3.2.2)

Total for two tracks: $q_t = 154 \times 2 = 308$ kN/m

For each beam (5 beams): $q = 308/5 = 61 \cdot 6$ kN/m

$$M_{qd} = 1 \cdot 5 q L^2 / 8 = 8735 \text{ kN m}$$

$$M_{Sd} = M_{gd} + M_{qd} = 16\,660 \text{ kN m}$$

Resistant moment at midspan, M_{Rd}

The tensile forces in the reinforcement are shown in Table F5, where d_s is the distance of the reinforcement from the top of the slab.

The reinforcement compressive force is shown in Table F6.

Concrete compressive force

$$F_{cc} = f_{cd} b y = 9619 \text{ kN}$$

where

$$f_{cd} = 0 \cdot 80 \times 35/1 \cdot 5 = 18 \cdot 6 \text{ N/mm}^2$$

$$b = 2420 \text{ mm}$$

$$y = 0 \cdot 8 x = 213 \text{ mm}$$

Total $F_c = F_{cc} + F_{sc} = 9804$ kN.

Resistant moment

$$\begin{aligned} M_{Rd} &= F_s(d_s - 0 \cdot 4 x) = 216 \times (2 \cdot 08 - 0 \cdot 11) + 307 \times (2 \cdot 47 - 0 \cdot 11) \\ &\quad + 9281 \times (2 \cdot 36 - 0 \cdot 11) \\ &= 426 + 725 + 20\,882 \\ &= 22\,033 \text{ kN m} \end{aligned}$$

Check

For $F_c = F_s$

$$M_{Rd} = 22\,033 > M_{Sd} = 16\,660$$

F5.2. Ultimate limit state at release of prestress (at 9·3 m from support)

Condition to be fulfilled

$$M_{Sd} \leqslant M_{Rd}$$

with

$$M_{Sd} = M(0 \cdot 9 g; \ 1 \cdot 2 P_0)$$

in accordance with Table 6.2 of MC78, and

$$M_{Rd} = M(0 \cdot 8 f_{ckj}/1 \cdot 5; f_y/1 \cdot 15; f_{0 \cdot 1k}/1 \cdot 15)$$

Fig. 4.4

4.1.3
Figs 2.1,
4.4, 2.6, 2.9

Acting moment, M_{Sd}
Prestressing force (section F4.5): $P_0 = -8556$ kN.

$$N_{pd} = 1 \cdot 2 P_0 = -10\,267 \text{ kN}$$

Acting prestressing moment

$$M_{pd} = 1 \cdot 2 P_0 e_p = -7598 \text{ kN m}$$

where $e_p = 0 \cdot 74$ m (Table F8).

Dead load moment (section F3.2.1)

$$M_{gd} = 0 \cdot 9 \times 25 \cdot 58 \times (9 \cdot 3/2) \times 18 \cdot 2 = 1948 \text{ kN m}$$

$$M_{Sd} = M_{pd} + M_{gd} = -5650 \text{ kN m}$$

Resistant moment, M_{Rd}
Given

$$f_{cdj} = 0 \cdot 8 \times 38/1 \cdot 5 = 20 \cdot 2 \text{ N/mm}^2$$

$$f_{sd} = 440/1 \cdot 15 = 382 \text{ N/mm}^2$$

where e_c is distance of compressive forces from centre.

Resistant compressive forces and moments are shown in Table F7.

Check
For $F_c = N_{pd}$

$$M_{Rd} = 5823 > M_{Sd} = 5650 \text{ kN m}$$

F5.3. Mechanical degree of prestressing   *3.1.2*
In midspan

$$\lambda = 10\,675/11\,731 = 0 \cdot 91$$

F5.4. Shear in web   *4.4*
Upper limit of resistant shear force   *4.4.2*
Condition to be fulfilled

$$V_{Sd} \leqslant V_{Rd}$$

with

$$V_{Sd} = V(1 \cdot 35g; \ 1 \cdot 5q)$$

$$V_{Rd} = V_{Rd2} + A_p \sigma_{p0} \sin \alpha_p$$

$$V_{Rd2} = 0 \cdot 30 f_{cd} b_w d$$

Determination of V_{Sd}
Dead load (section F3.2.1): $g = 62 \cdot 10$ kN/m.

$$V_{gd} = 1 \cdot 35 g L/2 = 1152 \text{ kN}$$

Live load (section F3.2.2)

Total for two tracks: $q_t = 172 \times 2 = 344$ kN

For each beam: $q = 344/5 = 68 \cdot 8$ kN

Table F7. *Resistant compressive forces and moments*

	e_c: m	A: mm^2	f_d: N/mm^2	F_c: kN	M_{Rd}: kN m
Four bars of 16 mm dia.	0·86	803	382	307	264
Five bars of 12 mm dia.	0·47	565	382	216	101
Concrete	0·56	482 490	20·2	9 746	5458
Total	—	—	—	10 269	5823

Fig.

$$V_{qd} = 1.5qL/2 = 1419 \text{ kN}$$

$$V_{Sd} = V_{gd} + V_{qd} = 2571 \text{ kN}$$

Determination of V_{Rd}

$$f_{cd} = 0.8 \times 50/1.5 = 26.6 \text{ N/mm}^2$$

$$b_w = 260 \text{ mm}$$

$$d = 2350 \text{ mm}$$

$$V_{Rd2} = 0.3 \times 26.6 \times 260 \times 2350 \times 10^{-3} = 4876 \text{ kN}$$

Neglecting the contribution of prestressing at the support, at 600 mm from the end of the beam and with $\sin \alpha_p \approx 0$

$$V_{Rd} = V_{Rd2}$$

Check

$$V_{Sd} = 2571 < V_{Rd} = 4876 \text{ kN}$$

Design of shear reinforcement   *4.4.2(b)*

Condition to be fulfilled

$$V_{Sd} \leqslant V_{wd} + V_{cd} + A_p \sigma_{p0} \sin \alpha_p$$

with

$$V_{wd} = 0.9d(A_{sw}/s)f_{ywd}$$

Taking into account that the bridge is affected by fatigue effects (MC78)

$$V_{cd} = 0$$

Furthermore (see above), the contribution of prestressing has been neglected.

Determination of V_{wd}

$$f_{ywd} = 440/1.15 = 382.6 \text{ N/mm}^2$$

$$d = 2350 \text{ mm}$$

$$A_{sw}/s = 4.52 \text{ mm (stirrups 2} \times \text{dia. 12 mm at 10 mm spacing)}$$

$$V_{wd} = 0.9 \times 2350 \times 4.52 \times 382.6 \times 10^{-3} = 3657 \text{ kN}$$

Check

$$V_{Sd} = 2571 < V_{wd} = 3657 \text{ kN}$$

F5.5. Detailing of shear reinforcement   *4.4.2(c)*

At end zone of beam

$$\rho_{w\,min} = 4.52/4.60 = 0.98\% > 0.15\%$$

Since $V_{Sd} < \frac{2}{3}V_{Rd2}$

$$s_{max} = 0.5d = 0.5 \times 2350 = 1175 \not> 300 \text{ mm}$$

$$s = 100 \text{ mm} < 300 \text{ mm}$$

6. Serviceability limit state checks

F6.1. Cross-section values   *5*

See Table F8.

F6.2. Structural analysis   *5.2*

Transverse distribution for beam 2

Bending and shear stresses in longitudinal beams and transverse   *5.2.1*
girders have been calculated with the deck modelled as a plane

elastic grid. This calculation shows that, in the elastic range, beam 2 has maximum stresses and deformations.

Figure F5 shows midspan deflections with loading on one track and loading on both tracks.

The following checks refer to beam 2.

Bending moments and shear forces   *5.1*

Table F9 shows the bending moments at midspan and the shear forces at the support due to the dead load of the beam, slab and ballast; prestressing; and live load.

F6.3. Concrete and steel stresses

F6.3.1. Stresses at midspan

Figure F6 shows stress diagrams due to different load conditions, shrinkage and creep effects.

F6.3.2. Stress redistribution due to creep   *5.2.2*

The effects of different creep coefficients for the beam and slab act on the stress distributions due to the dead load and prestressing (diagram (b) in Fig. F6).

Table F8. Cross-section values (including bonded reinforcement)

	In span		At support (0·60 m from end of beam)	
	Girder	Final section	Girder	Final section
Section area: m^2	0·932	1·525	1·438	2·030
Centre from bottom: m	0·890	1·469	0·990	1·390
Strands from centre: m	0·740	1·319	0·414	0·814
Moment of inertia: m^4	0·500	1·307	0·658	1·473
Moduli of inertia: m^3				
Slab top	—	1·267	—	1·333
Girder top	0·365	1·650	0·518	1·703
Girder strands	0·675	0·991	1·415	1·705
Bottom	0·561	0·889	0·664	1·060

Table F9. Bending moments and shear forces

	Action	Bending moment at midspan	Shear force at support	
Beam	g_0	2349	351	*5.1.1*
Slab	g_1	1399	204	*5.1.2*
Ballast	g_2	2080	303	*Table*
Live load	q	6000	1199	
Prestressing	P	—*	—†	

* See section F4.5.
† Neglected.

Table F10. Comparison of calculated stress values (N/mm^2)

	FIP recommendations	ID method
Slab		
Top	0·07	−0·04
Bottom	−0·72	−0·78
Girder		
Top	1·08	1·24
Bottom	−0·29	−0·37

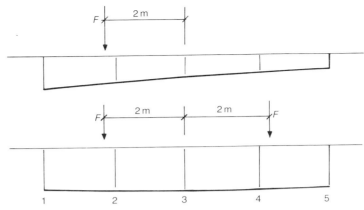

Fig. F5. Midspan deflections

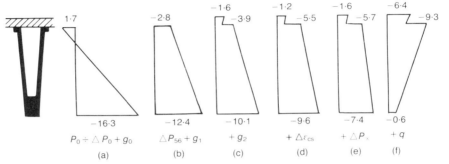

Fig. F6. Stresses at midspan (N/mm²)

This calculation has been carried out following section 5.2.2 of the recommendations using the ratio

$$\varphi/(1 + \varphi) = 0.637$$

The stress distribution thus calculated is compared with that obtained from a more theoretical step-by-step incremental solution (ID method). The results are shown in Table F10.

Diagram (e) in Fig. F6 shows the loss of prestress and the stress redistribution which are the final effects due to creep.

F6.3.3. Differential shrinkage

Stresses due to differential shrinkage between slab and beam have been calculated assuming

$$\Delta\varepsilon_{cs} = \varepsilon_{\infty, \text{slab}} - \varepsilon_{56, \text{beam}} = 0.0001$$

These effects are shown in diagram (d) in Fig. F6.

F6.3.4. Stress limit checks
Concrete in compression

$$\sigma_{cc} \leqslant 0.5 f_{ck}$$

At release of prestressing

girder: $f_{ckj} = 38$ N/mm², $\sigma_{cc} \leqslant 19$ N/mm², checked

In use

girder: $f_{ck} = 50$ N/mm², $\sigma_{cc} \leqslant 25$ N/mm², checked

slab: $f_{ck} = 35$ N/mm², $\sigma_{cc} \leqslant 17$ N/mm², checked

5.3

5.3.1

Table 2.1

Concrete in tension   5.3.2
Values are for good working conditions and high standard of control.

At release of prestressing   *Fig. 5..*

$f_{ck} = 38$ N/mm^2, $h = 300$ mm, $\sigma_{ct} \leqslant 2 \cdot 96$ N/mm^2,   checked

In use

σ_{ct} (extreme fibre) $\leqslant 0$,   checked   3.4.3(a

F6.3.5. Stresses in web

$f_{ctk} = 0 \cdot 7 f_{ctm} = 0 \cdot 7 \times 4 \cdot 8 = 3 \cdot 36$ N/mm^2

σ_{ct} (principal in web) $\leqslant 0 \cdot 75 f_{ctk} = 2 \cdot 52$ N/mm^2 3.4.3(a

At support ($b_0 = 460$ mm)

$\tau_{max} = 2 \cdot 08$ N/mm^2

$\sigma_c = -0 \cdot 65$ N/mm^2 (neglecting prestress contribution)

σ_{ct} (principal in web) $= 1 \cdot 78 < 2 \cdot 52$ N/mm^2

At $1 \cdot 30$ m from support ($b_0 = 260$ mm)

$\tau_{max} = 2 \cdot 90$ N/mm^2

$\sigma_c = -5 \cdot 24$ N/mm^2

σ_{ct} (principal in web) $= 1 \cdot 28 < 2 \cdot 52$ N/mm^2

F6.4. Deformations   5.4
Under permanent loading, deflections are almost balanced by prestressing (diagram (e) in Fig. F6).

Under live load in midspan, $\delta_{max} = 12 \cdot 2$ mm (calculation based on elasticity theory).

Values for comparison

$\delta/L = 12 \cdot 2/27\ 500 = 1/2250$

Slenderness $L/h = 27 \cdot 5/2 \cdot 5 = 11$

F6.5. Crack control   5.5
Under maximum live load

σ_{ct} (extreme fibre) < 0

F6.6. Degree of load-balancing   3.1.3

$K_p = 4740/5828 = 0 \cdot 81$

based on bending moments.

F7. Fatigue

F7.1. At midspan
Prestressing strands
The stress increment under live load must be less than $\Delta f_{sk}/\gamma =$ 4.8
$200/1 \cdot 5 = 133$ N/mm^2.

$\Delta\sigma_p = \alpha M_q/W_p = 5 \cdot 4 \times (6000/0 \cdot 991) \times 10^{-3} = 33 < 133$ N/mm^2

Reinforcing bars
The stress increment under live load must be less than $\Delta f_{sk}/\gamma =$ 4.8
$150/1 \cdot 5 = 100$ N/mm^2.

$\Delta\sigma_s = \alpha M_q/W_s = 5 \cdot 4 \times (6000/0 \cdot 908) \times 10^{-3} = 36 < 100$ N/mm^2

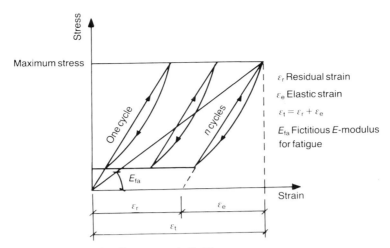

Fig. F7. Stress–strain diagram: definitions

Concrete

Fatigue in concrete is usually due to a reduction of compressive and tensile strength. In this case, as the maximum stresses in compression under the live load are less than $0.3f_{cd}$, the effect of fatigue on the compressive strength is negligible. Moreover, as the previous calculation shows that there are no tensile stresses, fatigue has no effect on tensile strength or on cracking.

However, the increase in residual strain due to fatigue (see Fig. F7) has the same effect as creep because it leads to further loss of prestress.

Neither MC78 nor the recommendations give explicit rules to check this effect.

A simple method is to consider a fictitious secant E-modulus

$$E_{fa} = 0.6E_{28}$$

So the increasing strain for fatigue is

$$\Delta\varepsilon_{fa} = \frac{\sigma_{cs}}{E_{28}}\left\{\frac{1 - 0.6}{0.6}\right\}$$

and the further loss of prestress is

$$\Delta P_{fa} = A_p E_s \Delta\varepsilon_{fa}$$

At midspan

$$\Delta P_{fa} = 196 \text{ kN}$$

The stress increment for fatigue is

top $\Delta\sigma_c = -0.08 \text{ N/mm}^2$

bottom $\Delta\sigma_c = 0.42 \text{ N/mm}^2$

F7.2. At support

The prestressing force at the support, 600 mm from the end of the beam, is

$$F_p = n\omega f_{bd} l_0$$

where n is number of strands $= 48$, $\omega = \pi\phi = \pi \times 15.2 = 47.7$ mm, $l_0 = 600$ mm, and $f_{bd} = 4.5$ N/mm^2 for concrete C50.

Fig. 6.5

The effects of fatigue on the concrete lead to a reduction of f_{bd}. Assuming $f_{bd\,fa} = 0.6f_{bd} = 2.7$ N/mm^2, then

$$F_p = 3709 \text{ kN}$$

Check

$$V_{Sd} \tan \theta \leqslant F_p \cos \alpha_p$$

$$2563 < 3705$$

Since the effects of fatigue in the anchorage zones are very danger-ous, additional reinforcement perpendicular to the strands has been provided in the zone of transfer of prestress, in order to increase the value of f_{bd}.

F8. Detailing

$c_h = 37$ mm > 20 mm

$c_v = 39$ mm > 10 mm

$l_t = 100\phi = 1330$ mm

Table

2.3.6

Example G   Silo at Schelklingen, Germany: large-capacity silo for cement clinker

Post-tensioned cylindrical shell

Example prepared by J. Peter (Stuttgart), with the assistance of M. Miehlbradt (Lausanne)

References to *FIP recommendations: Practical design of reinforced and prestressed concrete structures (based on the CEB–FIP model code (MC78))* are given in the right-hand margin

1. Introduction

G1.1. General

To guarantee a smooth and continuous production and delivery of cement, it is necessary to store different kinds of bulk solids, such as raw meal (ground limestone), cement clinker and cement—and also, recently, fly-ash or blast-furnace slag—in large quantities. For the storage of powdery materials such as cement, single circular silos with capacities of 4000–20 000 t and diameters of up to 30 m are frequently used.

Storage of cement clinker in outdoor areas is generally prohibited due to environmental restrictions, and is not desirable for operational reasons. Taking into account the fact that clinker has to be stored in very large quantities, special kinds of structure will be necessary, such as longitudinal or circular storage units up to a capacity of 150 000 t, or single circular silos up to 70 000 t or even more. For such large silo bins, a typical diameter of $d = 36$ m is required, with a depth of fill (surface of fill considered level) of about 40 m. In this case, the height/diameter ratio amounts to $h/d = 1.11$, which is quite normal for such types of silo. According to the German loading code DIN 1055 part 6, *Design loads for buildings: loads in silos*,[1] the silo pressure theory is only applicable for containment structures with $h/d \geqslant 0.8$. For structures with $h/d \leqslant 0.8$, the earth pressure theory has to be adopted.

G1.2. Prestressing of silo walls

Usually, silos are designed with horizontal prestressing in the walls. All other components (roof, silo base, foundations) are conventionally reinforced. The necessity for horizontal prestressing is decided individually. Where there are no special requirements on behalf of the client, this decision depends only on the size of the hoop tensile force, which is a function of the diameter, the height of the silo and the kind of material stored. The following numerical values are given as examples, not as general recommendations.

In principle, there is a simple rule: as long as the ordinary reinforcement around the diameter can be placed without any problems during construction of the silo wall (mostly by slipforming), no prestressing is necessary. The placing of a second layer of horizontal bars behind the vertical reinforcement should be avoided. Also, the bar spacing should not be less than 100 mm.

Where 28 mm bars are placed on the outside and 25 mm bars on the inside of the wall, the total area of reinforcement amounts to 11 070 mm²/m. This relates to a hoop tension of about 3000 kN/m, taking into account a working stress in the steel of approximately 280 N/mm² (S 500). However, with proper crack control in mind, it is recommended[2] not to go up to 3000 kN/m hoop tensile force, but to have a limit of about 2000–2300 kN/m. If the hoop tensile force exceeds this recommended value, prestressing should be applied. This is usually the case for clinker silos with diameters more than 20 m.

The prestressing forces chosen should not be too high, bearing in mind the temperature gradient in the silo wall, which can be very high for hot bulk materials. Full prestressing, in the sense of no tensile stress occurring due to loads or temperatures, is not really applicable. First of all, unnecessarily high compressive stresses would act at the inner face of the wall, due to prestressing and temperature, in a silo which was nearly empty. Secondly, full prestress would mitigate against either a wall which was only partly loaded by the bulk solids for quite long periods (partly filled) or a nearly empty silo with no dead load action in the horizontal direction: this would result in relatively high losses of the prestressing forces due to creep and shrinkage. And, thirdly, full prestress (overstressing) would prevent

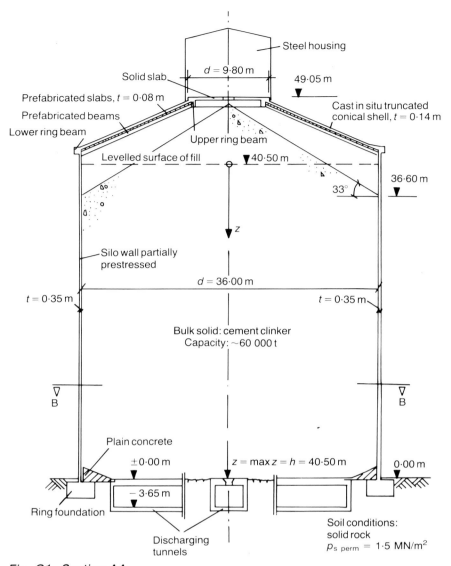

Fig. G1. Section AA

the occurrence of cracks, which is not desirable: the occurrence of cracks will reduce the stiffness of the silo wall and therefore also the restraining bending moments due to temperature, provided that proper crack control is exercised. In practice these considerations lead to the application of partial prestressing. For a reasonable degree of prestressing, see section G2.

The prestressing forces are normally produced by post-tensioned tendons which are embedded in the wall. There are two methods of placing tendons. In one method, the completely assembled tendons, consisting of (corrugated) ducts, internal wires or strands and anchorage elements, are placed horizontally in the wall during construction (slipforming). In the other method, rigid ducts only are fixed during slipforming, and wires or strands are pushed through the ducts and anchored after completion of the wall construction.

Stressing of the tendons (and injection of the ducts) is usually done at external buttresses. The minimum number of stressing points should be four, and for larger diameters, six. The tendons should form an overlapping pattern to compensate for any unequal distribution of the prestressing force due to friction around the silo circumference. For the same reason, all tendons should be stressed ringwise and from both ends simultaneously (see Fig. G2).

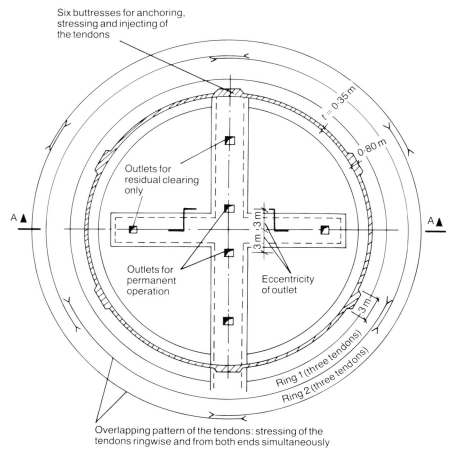

Six buttresses for anchoring,
stressing and injecting of
the tendons

Outlets for
residual clearing
only

Outlets for
permanent
operation

Eccentricity
of outlet

Ring 1 (three tendons)
Ring 2 (three tendons)

Overlapping pattern of the tendons: stressing of the
tendons ringwise and from both ends simultaneously

Fig. G2. Section BB

G1.3. Temperature in silos

Bulk solids in the cement industry are normally loaded warm, or even hot, into silos;[2] for example, cement is loaded at 80–100°C, and clinker at 120–180°C. These temperatures must be taken into account in the silo design. Different aspects must be considered, as follows.

In wall sections in direct contact with bulk solids, the heat flows quickly to the atmosphere outside and a non-stationary heat flow can be observed over a certain period. The bulk material directly next to the wall acts as an insulating layer. Therefore the stresses due to temperature within these wall sections can be neglected.

The air inside the silo above the surface of the bulk solids is heated considerably and a heat flow from the inside to the outside occurs through the areas which are in contact with the heated air (parts of the wall, roof). In a way, this is a stationary heat flow, because the process can be assumed constant for a certain period. Depending on the temperature of the bulk material at loading and the atmospheric temperature, a heat capacity calculation can be performed,[2] and the temperature gradient within the silo wall and roof can be determined.

G1.4. Silo at Schelklingen

The clinker silo which is the subject of this example was designed and constructed for the Heidelberger Zement Aktiengesellschaft plant at Schelklingen, FRG, in 1983.

The example relates to the design of the silo wall only, which is

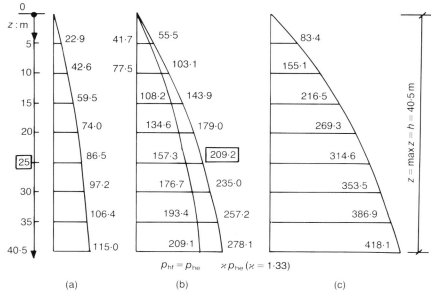

Fig. G3. Loads against silo wall: (a) wall friction load, p_{wf} (kN/m²); (b) horizontal loads, p_{hf}, p_{he} and κp_{he} (kN/m²); vertical load, p_{vf} (kN/m²)

partially prestressed in the horizontal direction, using post-tensioned tendons. Data regarding the other structural components are given for information only.

G2. Design information

G2.1. Description and system

See Figs G1 and G2.

External diameter: 36·70 m.

Height of the concrete structure above ground level: 49·05 m.

Roof: truncated conical shell, thickness 0·14 m, cast in situ on prefabricated reinforced concrete beams and slabs, supported by a temporary, centrally located scaffolding tower during construction stage.

Wall: cylindrical shell, thickness $t = 0·35$ m, inner diameter $d = 36·00$ m. The wall has partial prestressing in the horizontal direction, with post-tensioned tendons anchored, stressed and injected at six buttresses (Fig. G2). The edge conditions are as follows.

(a) *Upper edge.* The cast in situ roof shell is a stiffening member for preventing horizontal deformations.
(b) *Lower edge.* This is rigidly fixed into the foundation.

Foundation: ring foundation on solid rock; permissible soil pressure 1·5 MN/m².

Capacity 60 000 t

Filling height referring to a levelled surface: $h = 40·50$ m.

Volume: $\pi \times 18·0^2 \times 40·50 \approx 40\,000$ m³.

Unit weight for determination of capacity only: 1·5 t/m³.

Example calculation

The loading conditions are considered here for the silo wall only, and the calculation refers to the design of the horizontal prestressed and non-prestressed reinforcement for one section at level $z = 25$ m (see Figs G3 and G4). The internal forces at this section consist of normal forces only. Bending moments in the vertical (meridional) direction are caused only at small areas along the edges of the wall and are not considered here.

G2.2. Loading conditions
G2.2.1. General
As Appendix 1 of the recommendations does not refer to loads in silos, the loads (pressure) against the silo wall are assumed in accordance with the German loading code DIN 1055 part 6, *Design loads for buildings: loads in silos*. Possible vibration phenomena during emptying are to be avoided by structural means.

Data for clinker [3.1.1]*
Unit weight: $\gamma = 18 \text{ kN/m}^3$ [*Table 1*]*
Horizontal load ratio: $\lambda = 0.50$
Coefficient of wall friction for medium-smooth wall (e.g. slipform concrete): $\mu_2 = 0.55$
Factor for loads due to emptying: $e_h = 1.20$
Factor for bulk solid: $\beta_G = 0.70$

Hydraulic radius [3.1.2]*
The shape and size of the cross-section are generally taken into account through the ratio of cross-sectional area to perimeter, A/u (hydraulic radius). For circular cross-section

$$A/u = d/4 = 36.0/4 = 9.0 \text{ m}$$

G2.2.2. Loads due to filling [3.2]*
Wall friction load

$$p_{wf}(z) = \frac{\gamma A}{u}\, \phi(z) = 18 \times 9.0\phi(z) = 162.0\phi(z) \text{ kN/m}^2$$

Horizontal load

$$p_{hf}(z) = \frac{\gamma A}{\mu u}\, \phi(z) = \frac{18 \times 9.0}{0.55}\, \phi(z) = 294.5\phi(z) \text{ kN/m}^2$$

Vertical load (not applicable to silo wall; for information only)

$$p_{vf}(z) = \frac{\gamma A}{\lambda \mu u}\, \phi(z) = \frac{18 \times 9.0}{0.50 \times 0.55}\, \phi(z) = 589.1\phi(z) \text{ kN/m}^2$$

The first term signifies the load at unlimited depth, and

$$\phi(z) = 1 - e^{-z/z_0}$$

with

$$z_0 = \frac{A}{\lambda \mu u} = \frac{9.0}{0.50 \times 0.55} = 32.727 \text{ m}$$

signifies the increase of the load depending on the depth z.

For the distribution of the loads p_{wf}, p_{hf} and p_{vf} over the depth z, see Fig. G3.

G2.2.3. Loads due to emptying
Uniformly distributed loads. [3.3]*
[3.3.2]*

Wall friction load: $p_{we} = e_w p_{wf}$

Horizontal load: $p_{he} = e_h p_{hf}$

Vertical load: $p_{ve} < p_{vf}$

---

* DIN 1055, part 6.[1]

$$\frac{h}{d\mu} = \frac{40 \cdot 50}{36 \cdot 0 \times 0 \cdot 55} = 2 \cdot 05 < 2 \cdot 5$$

This means that the silo can be considered as a 'shallow bin' with $p_{we} = p_{wf}$ and $p_{he} = p_{hf}$.

For a non-uniformly distributed horizontal load, there are two different concepts: application of a local load, or increase of the uniformly distributed load by a magnifying factor κ. The latter concept will be adopted here.

[3.3.3]
[3.3.3.
[3.3.3.

As the silo has a circular cross-section and ratio $r/t = 18 \cdot 0/0 \cdot 35 = 51 < 70$

$$\kappa = 1 \cdot 0 + 0 \cdot 5\beta + 0 \cdot 02\beta r/t$$

where r is radius of silo, and t is wall thickness.

Non-uniform load factor

[3.3.3.

$$\beta = \beta_h \beta_a \beta_r \beta_G$$

Height/diameter factor

$$\beta_h = 0 \cdot 2\frac{h}{d} + 0 \cdot 8$$

$$= 0 \cdot 2 \times \frac{40 \cdot 5}{36 \cdot 0} + 0 \cdot 8 = 1 \cdot 025 \quad \begin{cases} > 1 \cdot 0 \\ < 1 \cdot 6 \end{cases}$$

Eccentricity of outlet: $a = 3 \cdot 0$ m (see Fig. G2). Ratio $a/r = 3 \cdot 0/18 \cdot 0 = 1/6 < 1/3$ gives eccentricity factor

$$\beta_a = 1 \cdot 0$$

Ratio $r/t < 70$ gives rigidity factor

$$\beta_r = 0 \cdot 30$$

Factor for bulk solid: $\beta_G = 0 \cdot 70$. Therefore

[Tabl

$$\beta = 1 \cdot 025 \times 1 \cdot 0 \times 0 \cdot 30 \times 0 \cdot 70 = 0 \cdot 215$$

$$\kappa = 1 \cdot 0 + 0 \cdot 5 \times 0 \cdot 215 + 0 \cdot 02 \times 0 \cdot 215 \times \frac{18 \cdot 0}{0 \cdot 35} = 1 \cdot 33$$

Horizontal load to be applied for loading case emptying (critical)

$$\kappa p_{he} = 1 \cdot 33 \, p_{he}$$

(see Fig. G3).

G2.3. Internal forces on silo wall
Horizontal ring tensile (hoop) forces

$$n_9 = \kappa p_{he} r$$
$$= 1 \cdot 33 p_{he} \times 18 \cdot 0 \text{ kN/m}$$

Figure G4 shows the distribution of the horizontal ring tensile forces both for the membrane state (according to the formula above) and for the real supporting conditions of the silo wall at its lower edge, considering an unloaded area due to the annular plain concrete wedge (see Fig. G1) and the fixing of the wall into the ring foundation.

Vertical forces
Weight of roof: $n_\varphi = 94 \cdot 0$ kN/m.

Dead weight: $n_\varphi = 0 \cdot 35 \times 25z = 8 \cdot 75z$ kN/m.

* DI
part (

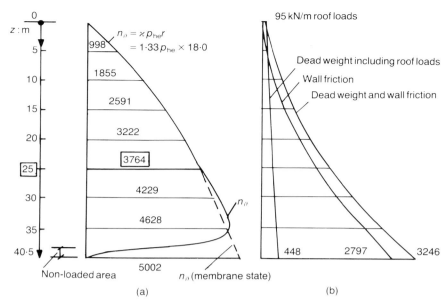

Fig. G4. Internal forces of silo wall: (a) horizontal tensile forces, n_ϑ (kN/m); (b) vertical forces, n_φ (kN/m)

The total wall friction load from the levelled surface of the fill to depth z

$$n_\varphi = \int_0^z p_{wf}(z) \, dz = \frac{\gamma A}{u}(z - z_0 \, \phi(z))$$

$$= 162 \cdot 0(z - 32 \cdot 727 \phi(z)) \text{ kN/m}$$

For the distribution of these loads see Fig. G4.

G2.4. Materials
G2.4.1. Data for concrete
C30   *2.1.1*

Characteristic compressive strength: $f_{ck} = 30$ N/mm².   *2.1.2*
Modulus of elasticity (mean value): $E_{cm} = 32$ kN/mm².   *2.1.5*
                                                                                     Fig. 2.4

   Shrinkage and creep   *2.1.7*

$$\frac{2A_c}{u} = t = 0 \cdot 35 \text{ m}$$

Atmospheric conditions: dry.

t_0: medium (7–60 days).

Shrinkage: $\varepsilon_{cs}(t_\infty, t_0) = 0 \cdot 31 \times 10^{-3}$.   *Table 2.1*

Creep: $\phi(t_\infty, t_0) = 3 \cdot 0$.

Time of stressing 28 days after completion of slipforming

   $\phi_1/\phi_\infty = 0 \cdot 25$ *Fig. 2.5*

G2.4.2. Data for steel   *2.2*
  Reinforcing steel   *2.2.1*
S 500
Characteristic strength: $f_{yk} = 500$ N/mm².   *2.2.2*

  Prestressing steel (VSL system)   *2.3*
Strands 0·6 in (15·2 mm), S 1570/1770.   *2.3.1*

Characteristic strength: $f_{0 \cdot 1k} = 1570$ N/mm².   *2.3.2*

Characteristic tensile strength: $f_{tk} = 1770$ N/mm^2.

Modulus of elasticity: $E_p = 195$ kN/mm^2 (according to approval   *2.3.5*
document).

Relaxation of prestressing steel   *2.3.3*
Where the controlling stress in the prestressing steel amounts to
$\sigma_p = 1100$ N/mm^2, the losses due to steel relaxation can be deter-
mined as follows.

$$\sigma_p / f_{tk} = 1100/1770 \approx 0.62$$

Steel group 2   *Fig.*

Loss (final value): 4%

Considering temperature effects, this value is doubled to 8%.[3]

For the stress σ_p, see also the stress condition adopted (section G5.2)
and the calculation (section G7).

G3. Principal arrangement of reinforcement and tendons in silo wall

See Fig. G5.

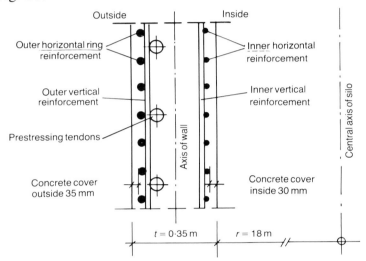

Fig. G5. Arrangement of reinforcement and tendons

G4. Wall thickness

The determination of the wall thickness is more or less a matter of
experience. The vertical loads are rather low. In the case of prestressed silo walls, account must be taken of the horizontal compressive stresses in the concrete due to prestressing when the silo is
empty, but for partial prestressing, these stresses have no influence
on the determination of the wall thickness. Therefore mainly matters
of serviceability and simple execution should be considered: sufficient concrete cover, easy assembly of the reinforcement and
tendons, and pouring and compacting of the concrete without any
complications.

Wall thickness adopted: $t = 0.35$ m.

G5. Serviceability limit state

G5.1. Horizontal reinforcement and prestressing tendons; degree of prestressing

The total horizontal ring tensile forces have to be allocated to the
reinforcement and tendons only. The concrete has to be considered
to be fully cracked.

Referring to section G1.2, a combination of prestressing tendons

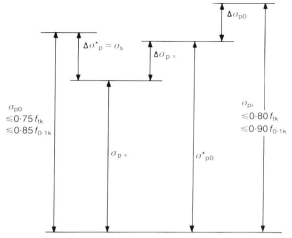

Fig. G6. Combination of stresses (serviceability limit state)

and reinforcing steel should be adopted for ring tensile forces exceeding approximately 2000 kN/m.

For reasons explained in section G1.2, partial prestressing should be adopted. As already stated, there is no dead weight action (no permanent load) in the horizontal direction, and the degree of load-balancing relates to the loading due to the bulk-solid live load only. As a matter of experience, about 50–60% of the ring tensile force should be allocated to the prestressing tendons, and the remainder to the reinforcing steel. This relates to the following degree of prestressing   *3.4.3(c)*   *3.1.3*

$$\kappa_p = \frac{\tilde{n}_\vartheta}{n_\vartheta} = 0.50\text{–}0.70$$

where n_ϑ is the maximum tensile force, and $\tilde{n}_\vartheta$ is that part of the tensile force for which, in combination with the prestressing force after shrinkage, creep and relaxation, the strain or stress will be zero (decompression). In that case

$$\tilde{n}_\vartheta = P_{m\infty}$$

where $P_{m\infty}$ is the mean value of the prestressing force at $t = \infty$.   *3.4.2*

Therefore, in accordance with section G2.3

$$\kappa_p = \frac{P_{m\infty}}{n_\vartheta}$$

i.e.

$$n_\vartheta \kappa_p - P_{m\infty} = 0$$

and

$$P_{m\infty} = \kappa_p n_\vartheta = \kappa_p \kappa p_{he}\, r$$

G5.2. Stress condition

According to a method described by Peter,[2] the equality of the strains of the prestressing and reinforcing steel for the cracked section leads to the following stress equation

$$\sigma_{p\infty} + \sigma_s = \sigma^*_{p\infty} + \Delta\sigma_{p\infty} + \sigma_s = \sigma_{p0}$$

The complete combination of stresses is shown in Fig. G6, where

σ_{p0} is stress limit which should not be exceeded ($\leqslant 0.75 f_{tk}$ or $\leqslant 0.85 f_{0.1k}$)   *3.2.1(b)*

$\Delta\sigma_p^*$ is stress increase in the prestressing steel after decompression $(=\sigma_s)$

σ_s is stress in the reinforcing steel after decompression

$\sigma_{p\infty}$ is stress in the prestressing steel after all losses $(t = \infty)$

$\Delta\sigma_{p\infty}$ is time-dependent loss of stress in the prestressing steel due to shrinkage, creep and relaxation   *3.3.3*

σ_{p0}^* is stress in the prestressing steel at $t = 0$

$\Delta\sigma_{p0}$ is stress difference for taking care of immediate losses due to friction (and draw-in, if required)   *3.3.2*

σ_{pi} is initial stress in the prestressing steel at the moment of tensioning ($\leqslant 0\cdot80 f_{tk}$ or $\leqslant 0\cdot90 f_{0\cdot1k}$).   *3.2.1*

The stress equation above applies only if $|\Delta\sigma_{p\infty}| \leqslant \sigma_s$. If $|\Delta\sigma_{p\infty}| > \sigma_s$, the stress σ_{p0} can be reduced or σ_s increased.

For practical design it is recommended that a certain area of the prestressing steel, A_p, should be applied, on the basis of an assumed arrangement of tendons (as a result of a preliminary design).

The fraction of the tensile force n_{ϑ} to be taken by the prestressing tendons is

$$P_{m0} = \sigma_{p0} A_p$$

The fraction of the tensile force n_{ϑ} to be taken by the reinforcing steel is

$$F_s = n_{\vartheta} - P_{m0} = n_{\vartheta} - \sigma_{p0} A_p$$

The area of reinforcing steel is

$$A_s = \frac{F_s}{\sigma_s}$$

Time-dependent losses   *3.3.3*

$$\Delta\sigma_{p\infty} = \frac{\varepsilon_s(t, t_0)E_p + \Delta\sigma_{pr} + \alpha\phi(t, t_0)\rho_p(\sigma_{p0} - \sigma_s)}{1 - \rho_p \alpha\left\{\dfrac{\phi(t, t_0)}{2} - 1\right\}}$$

where $\alpha = E_p/E_c$ and $\rho_p = A_p/A_c$.

$$\Delta P_\infty = \Delta\sigma_{p\infty} A_p$$

$$P_{m\infty} = A_p(\sigma_{p0} - \sigma_s)$$

$$P_{m0}^* = P_{m\infty} - \Delta P_\infty \quad (\Delta P_\infty \text{ negative})$$

Degree of prestressing

$$\kappa_p = \frac{P_{m\infty}}{n_{\vartheta}}$$

$$\sigma_{p0}^* = \frac{P_{m0}^*}{A_p}$$

$$\sigma_{p\infty} = \frac{P_{m\infty}}{A_p}$$

$$\Delta\sigma_p^* = \sigma_s = \frac{n_{\vartheta} - P_{m\infty}}{A_p + A_s}$$

G5.3. Crack control without high-temperature effects   *5.5*

Combinations of actions: frequent.   *5.1.2*

Tab.

$G = 0$ (no permanent load in horizontal direction)

$P = P_{m\infty}$

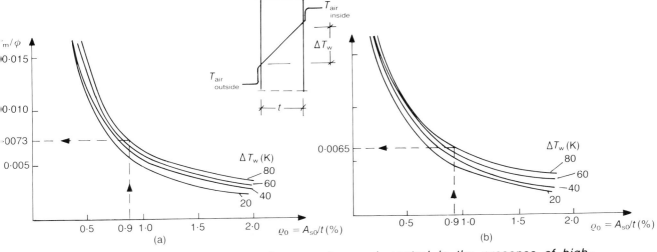

Fig. G7. Design diagrams for crack control in the presence of high-temperature effects, according to Peter:[2] (a) diagram V6c—$t = 0.35$ m, $P_{m\infty} = -1500$ kN/m, $n_\vartheta = 2500$ kN/m (n_ϑ^0); (b) diagram V7c—$t = 0.35$ m, $P_{m\infty} = -2500$ kN/m, $n_\vartheta = 3500$ kN/m (n_ϑ^0)

$$Q_1 = n_\vartheta$$

$\psi_1 = 1/\kappa$ (This is in accordance with the explanations to the German loading code DIN 1055 part 6,[1] section 3.3.3(11), according to which only the uniformly distributed load n_ϑ^0 can be considered as the frequent load action.)

$$\psi_1 Q_1 = n_\vartheta/\kappa = n_\vartheta^0$$

$$G + P + \psi_1 Q_1 = n_\vartheta^0 - P_{m\infty}$$

Controlling stress in the reinforcing steel for crack control

$$\sigma_s^* = \frac{1}{A_s}(n_\vartheta^0 - P_{m\infty})$$

$$P_{m\infty} = \kappa_p \kappa n_\vartheta^0$$

$$\sigma_s^* = n_\vartheta^0 \frac{1}{A_s}(1 - \kappa_p \kappa)$$

For limit values for steel stress and bar spacing, Fig. 5.4 of the recommendations should be used.   *Fig. 5.4*

G5.4. Minimum reinforcement
5.5.6

A minimum amount of reinforcement should be provided for all load-bearing members.

$$\rho_{r\,min} = \frac{A_s}{A_{c\,ef}}$$

The thickness h_{ef} should be in accordance with Fig. 5.4 of the recommendations.   *Fig. 5.4*

Minimum reinforcement is given by Fig. 5.5 of the recommendations.   *Fig. 5.5*

G5.5. Crack control including high-temperature effects

Regarding the high temperature of the cement clinker mentioned in section G1.3, special consideration is necessary, because control of cracking due to a high temperature gradient within the silo wall is not covered by the minimum reinforcement obtained by the procedure described above.

Design diagrams have been developed by Peter,[2] depending on

(a) wall thickness, t
(b) effective tension force, n_9°
(c) temperature difference across the silo wall, ΔT_w
(d) percentage of reinforcing steel placed at the outside, $\rho = A_{so}/t$ (%)
(e) crack width, w_m.

For all diagrams concerning prestressing, the distribution of the reinforcing steel is established at 67% at the outside of the silo wall and 33% at the inside.

The diagrams are based on the determination of the mean crack width w_m.

For normal durability requirements usually acceptable for silos, the limit of the crack width is considered to be $w_m = 0.15$ mm, but in no case should the value $w_m = 0.18$ mm be exceeded. Two examples of such diagrams are shown in Fig. G7.

G6. Ultimate limit state

Design principle: $S_d \leqslant R_d$. *1.2*

Design load effect

$$S_d = \gamma_q Q_1$$ *4.1.2*

$$G = 0$$

$$Q_1 = n_9^\circ$$

The controlling hoop tensile force at serviceability limit state, $n_9 = \kappa p_{he} r$, takes into account the uniformly distributed emptying loads plus the action of local load peaks (see comments on section 3.3.3 of DIN 1055 part 6[1]). However, the action of these load peaks (non-uniformly distributed loads) will virtually disappear due to the plastic behaviour of the silo wall in the horizontal direction up to ultimate limit state (ULS). Therefore the uniformly distributed load n_9° only can be considered as the controlling force for the ULS.

Partial safety coefficient for ULS action: $\gamma_q = 1.5$. *Table*

$$S_d = 1.5 n_9^\circ$$

Resistant action effects *4.1.3*
Partial safety coefficient for prestressing and reinforcing steel: $\gamma_s = 1.15$.

$$R_d = \frac{f_{0.1k} A_p}{\gamma_s} + \frac{f_{yk} A_s}{\gamma_s}$$

G7. Calculation

$n_9 = 3764$ kN/m at level $z = 25$ m (Fig. G4).

Using VSL system.

VSL 6–7: seven strands 0.6 in (15.3 mm).

S1570/1770 ($f_{0.1k}/f_{tk}$), in accordance with approval document. *2.3.1*

A_p per tendon: 980 mm^2.

Spacing of tendons: 440 mm.

$$A_p = (980/440) \times 1000 = 2227 \text{ mm}^2/\text{m}$$

$$\sigma_{p0} \leqslant \begin{cases} 0 \cdot 75 \times 1770 = 1328 \text{ N/mm}^2 \\ 0 \cdot 85 \times 1570 = 1335 \text{ N/mm}^2 \end{cases}$$

3.2.1(b)

The stress σ_{p0} should not be taken too high, so as to reduce the losses of the prestressing force due to shrinkage, creep and relaxation; to reduce the prestressing force and thus be able to use a sufficient amount of reinforcing steel for crack control; and to have enough margin in the initial stress σ_{pi} for taking care of the losses due to friction and draw-in.

Adopted stress: $\sigma_{p0} = 1100$ N/mm^2.

$$P_{m0} = 2227 \times 1100/1000 = 2450 \text{ kN/m}$$

$$F_s = 3764 - 2450 = 1314 \text{ kN/m}$$

Adopted stress for the reinforcing steel S500: $\sigma_s = 280$ N/mm^2.

$$A_s = (1314/280) \times 1000 = 4693 \text{ mm}^2/\text{m}$$

Time-dependent losses

2.1.5

$$E_c = 32 \text{ kN/mm}^2, \text{ C30}$$

$$E_p = 195 \text{ kN/mm}^2 = 1 \cdot 95 \times 10^5 \text{ N/mm}^2$$

$$\alpha = 195/32 = 6 \cdot 09$$

$$\rho_p = 2227/(350 \times 1000) = 0 \cdot 00636 \ (= 0 \cdot 636\%)$$

$$\varepsilon_s(t, t_0) = -31 \times 10^{-5}(1 - 0 \cdot 25) = -23 \cdot 25 \times 10^{-5}$$

$$\phi(t, t_0) = 3 \cdot 0(1 - 0 \cdot 25) = 2 \cdot 25$$

$$\Delta\sigma_{pr} \approx -0 \cdot 08 \times 1100 = -88 \text{ N/mm}^2$$

$$\Delta\sigma_{p\infty} = [-23 \cdot 25 \times 10^{-5} \times 1 \cdot 95 \times 10^5 - 88 \cdot 0 - 6 \cdot 09 \times 2 \cdot 25$$
$$\times 0 \cdot 006\,36 \times (1100 - 280)]/$$
$$[1 - 0 \cdot 006\,36 \times 6 \cdot 09 \times (2 \cdot 25/2 - 1)]$$
$$= \frac{-45 \cdot 3 - 88 \cdot 0 - 71 \cdot 5}{0 \cdot 995} = -206 \text{ N/mm}^2$$

$$\text{gives } |\Delta\sigma_{p\infty}| < \sigma_s$$

$$\Delta P_{\infty} = -206 \times 2227/1000 = -459 \text{ kN/m}$$

$$P_{m\infty} = 2227 \times (1100 - 280)/1000 = 1826 \text{ kN/m}$$

$$P_{m0}^* = 1826 - (-459) = 2285 \text{ kN/m}$$

Time-dependent losses in relation to P_{m0}^*

$$|\Delta P_{\infty}|/P_{m0}^* = 459/2285 = 0 \cdot 201 \ (20 \cdot 1\%)$$

Degree of prestressing

$$\kappa_p = 1826/3764 = 0 \cdot 49 \approx 0 \cdot 50$$

$$\sigma_{p0}^* = 2285 \times 1000/2227 = 1026 \text{ N/mm}^2 < \sigma_{p0} = 1100$$

Loss due to steel relaxation depends on σ_{p0}^*; no corrections → safe side.

$$\sigma_{p\infty} = 1826 \times 1000/2227 = 820 \text{ N/mm}^2$$

The stress increase in the prestressing steel at time $t = \infty$ must be equal to the applied stress in the reinforcing steel

$$\Delta\sigma_p^* = \frac{3764 - 1826}{2227 + 4693} \times 1000 = 280 \text{ N/mm}^2 = \sigma_s$$

Crack control without high-temperature effects

$n_{\vartheta}^{\circ} = 157 \cdot 3 \times 18 \cdot 0 = 2831 \ \text{kN/m}$

$A_s = 4693 \ \text{mm}^2/\text{m}$

Reinforcement provided

Outside: $\phi = 20 \ \text{mm}$, $s = 100 \ \text{mm}$; gives 3141 mm²/m $\approx 61\%$

Inside: $\phi = 16 \ \text{mm}$, $s = 100 \ \text{mm}$; gives 2011 mm²/m $\approx 39\%$

$A_{s \ ef} = \overline{5152 \ \text{mm}^2/\text{m}} \approx 100\%$

$> 4693 \ \text{mm}^2/\text{m}$

$\sigma_s^* = \dfrac{1}{5152} (2831 - 1826) \times 1000 = 195 \ \text{N/mm}^2$

For bar spacing $s \leqslant 100 \ \text{mm}$

$\sigma_s^* = 200 \ \text{N/mm}^2$ *Fig. 5*

$> 195 \ \text{N/mm}^2$

Minimum reinforcement

$A_s = 5152 \ \text{mm}^2/\text{m}$

Concrete cover outside: 35 mm.

Concrete cover inside: 30 mm.

$h_{ef} = 35 + 8 \times 20 + 8 \times 16 + 30 = 353 \ \text{mm} > 350 \ \text{mm}$ *Fig. 5*

$h_{ef} = t = 350 \ \text{mm}$

$\rho_{ef} = \dfrac{5152}{350 \times 1000} \times 100 = 1 \cdot 47\%$

Bar spacing: $s = 100 \ \text{mm}$.

$\rho_{r \ min} = 0 \cdot 44\% < 1 \cdot 47\%$ *Fig. 5*

The reinforcement provided is much more than the required minimum reinforcement.

Crack control including high-temperature effects
Application of the design diagrams Fig. G7.

$t = 0 \cdot 35 \ \text{m} = 350 \ \text{mm}$

$P_{m\infty} = 1826 \ \text{kN/m}$

$n_{\vartheta}^{\circ} = 2831 \ \text{kN/m}$

Reinforcing steel

$A_{so} = 3141 \ \text{mm}^2/\text{m} \ (\phi = 20 \ \text{mm}, s = 100 \ \text{mm})$

$A_{si} = 2011 \ \text{mm}^2/\text{m}$

Distribution: 61%/39% $\approx$ 67%/33%

$\rho_0 = \dfrac{3141}{350 \times 1000} \times 100 = 0 \cdot 90\%$

Diagram V6c ($t = 0 \cdot 35 \ \text{m}$, $P_{m\infty} = -1500 \ \text{kN/m}$, $n_{\vartheta} = 2500 \ \text{kN/m}$)

$\dfrac{w_m}{\phi} = 0 \cdot 0073$

gives

$$w_m = 0.0073 \times 20 = 0.146 \text{ mm}$$
$$\approx 0.15 \text{ mm}$$

Diagram V7c ($t = 0.35$ m, $P_{m\infty} = -2500$ kN/m, $n_\vartheta = 3500$ kN/m)

$$\frac{w_m}{\phi} = 0.0065$$

gives

$$w_m = 0.0065 \times 20 = 0.13 \text{ mm}$$
$$< 0.15 \text{ mm}$$

Even for the maximum temperature difference included in the diagrams, $\Delta T_w = 80°$K, the controlling crack width is not exceeded.

Ultimate limit state

$$S_d = 1.5 \times 2831 = 4247 \text{ kN/m}$$

$$R_d = \frac{1570 \times 2227}{1.15 \times 1000} + \frac{500 \times 5152}{1.15 \times 1000}$$
$$= 3040 + 2240 = 5280 \text{ kN/m} > S_d$$

Ultimate limit state is not critical.

References

1. *Design loads for buildings: loads in silos.* German Standards Institution, Berlin, 1987, DIN 1055, part 6 (standard and separate comments).
2. Peter J. Berechnung von Siloanlagen: Lastannahmen. Silos aus Stahlbeton und Spannbeton: freistehende kreiszylindrische Silos. *Silo Handbuch* (ed. Martens P.). Ernst, Berlin, 1988, sections 7.1 and 7.2.1.
3. *Complements to MC78.* Comité Euro-International du Béton, Lausanne, 1981, Bulletin d'Information 139, 72–74.

Example H   Grindel business centre, Bassersdorf, Switzerland: flat-slab office building

Partial prestressing of flat slabs with unbonded tendons

Example prepared by T. Friedrich (Zürich), with the assistance of J. Appleton (Lisbon) and M. Miehlbradt (Lausanne)

References to *FIP recommendations: Practical design of reinforced and prestressed concrete structures (based on the CEB–FIP model code (MC78))* are given in the right-hand margin

Introduction

H1.1. Partial prestressing

Prestressed flat slabs offer the engineer the opportunity to combine prestressing and ordinary reinforcement in a very successful manner.

The bending moments in a flat slab vary enormously. The elastic bending moments over the intermediate supports are up to five times as high as those in the middle strips. The prestressing tendons are, naturally, used where the highest resistance is required. The moments in the middle strips can generally be resisted by normal reinforcing steel. Sometimes the required minimum reinforcement alone will provide just enough resisting moment. Using only a small amount of prestressing, even concentrated within the column strips, will enormously improve deformation properties. For crack control, it is essential to use normal reinforcement.

Combining prestressing steel with normal reinforcement in such a way that the requirements (resistance, deformation and crack control) will be met, will lead to a robust structural system. Thus, optimum use is made of the different materials—concrete, prestressing and normal steels.

H1.2. Grindel building

The following design for the Grindel building was first prepared according to the new Swiss code SIA 162 (1989). Fig. H1 shows the building under construction. Fig. H2 gives the overall dimensions of most of the seven floors. The first two floors will be used for parking, the next two floors for storage and the last three as offices. Live loads vary from 2·5 kN/m² to 15·0 kN/m² and the respective structural slab thicknesses vary from 250 mm to 360 mm. Each floor covers about 3000 m², giving an overall area of almost 22 000 m². All slabs at all levels are prestressed by the column strip method. Calculations are given for one floor which will be used for offices. Special care was taken with the first two floors, which will be completely below ground. The walls and piled foundation slab will be subjected to soil and water pressures. In order to achieve watertightness, the foundation slab and walls were prestressed horizontally.

The structural system used for the whole building is characterized by flat slabs supported on columns. Overall horizontal stability is provided by four cores, shown in Fig. H2.

Apart from the normal advantages of prestressed flat slab construction—strength, deformations etc.—in this case prestressing also resulted in rapid construction progress. Progress was assisted by

Fig. H1. Building under construction

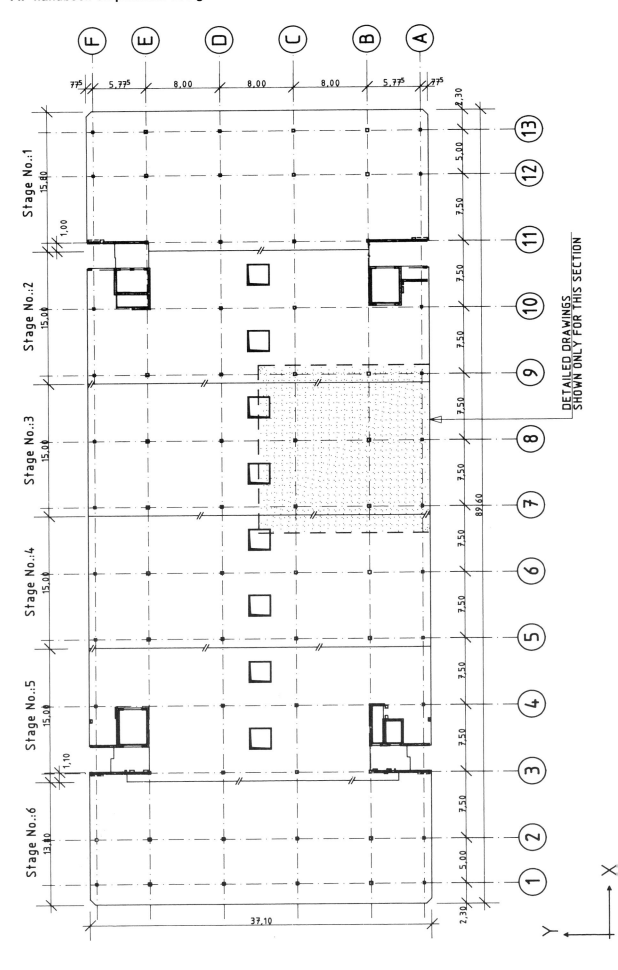

the use of prefabricated columns. Each floor was divided into six stages, each of about 550 m². The concrete volumes varied with the slab thicknesses from 140 m³ to 200 m³. On average, twelve columns had to be placed for each stage, and the general programme was as follows.

Monday	Apply prestress
	Remove scaffolding to new location
Tuesday	Adjust scaffolding at new location
	Set prefabricated columns in position
	Stabilize columns using scaffolding
	Start bottom reinforcement
Wednesday	Lay tendons
	Place top reinforcement
Thursday	Concrete the area
Friday to Monday	Allow concrete to set

Initial prestress was applied after three days. When the scaffolding was removed, only the vertical forces of the prestress supported the flat slab. The prestress, together with the concrete strength, was sufficient: there was no problem with deformation, as the dead load was completely compensated by the tendons.

This special construction method, using prestressed flat slabs and prefabricated columns, made it possible to complete the whole building within one year.

H1.3. Prestressing system and layout of tendons

Prestressing system

For flat slab construction in general, unbounded tendons are used. The small diameters of the tendons and the low friction values are advantageous in slender structures. Unbonded tendons need intermediate anchors to prevent the whole tendon from being destroyed by a localized accident.

Tendon layout

There are a number of alternative layouts which can be adopted for the tendons. The best results can be obtained if all the tendons are located within the column strip. Using the vertical component of the prestressing force to support the balanced load of the slab reduces the deformation by 75%. To eliminate the remaining 25% of this deformation, an equal amount of prestressing to that already used in midspan of the column strip will be needed. In addition, the necessary resistance outside the column strips can be obtained using ordinary reinforcement. In most cases the required minimum reinforcement will suffice. In general, there is no need for overall prestressing. High loads or strict deformation limits may, however, enforce the use of such prestressing.

Tendon profile

Tendons are generally parabolic in profile. For simpler design and construction, a trapezoidal profile may be considered. Tendons will be at the top of the slab over supports and in the bottom from the quarter-span. In between the profile is straight and at the change points the curvature is kept to a minimum (see Fig. H4). Only a few chairs are used, saving time during drawing and construction.

H1.4. Design process

The design procedure is based on the theory of plasticity. This method gives the designer considerable freedom in finding a suitable

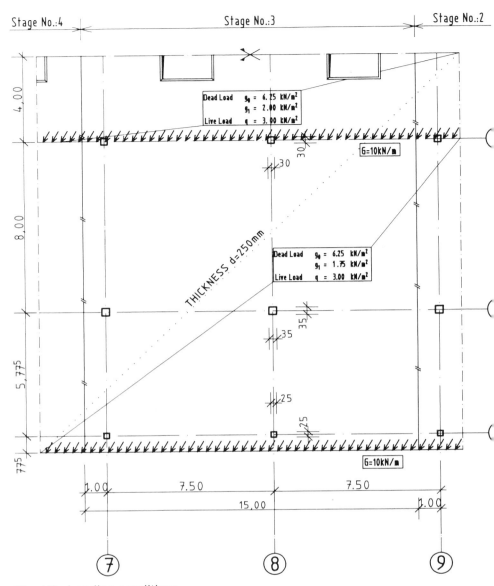

Fig. H3. Loading conditions

layout of prestressing steel and ordinary reinforcement. Serviceability checks are also simple, since the prestress eliminates the main part of the deformation and the resulting applied moments are, in general, too small to cause severe cracking.

When the design is complete, all information needs to be put on drawings for use on site. Drawings are needed for both prestressing steel and ordinary reinforcement, adding to the cost. Nowadays, computer-aided design (CAD) can have a great impact on this part of the design process, as many graphical tools provided by CAD systems can shorten the drawing process dramatically. Areas of reinforcement can easily be indicated and repeated at different points on the drawings. Cutting schedules can be produced automatically and tendon details, such as anchors, can be drawn by a parametric approach. The figures show typical parts of CAD drawings.

There is no need to draw the cross-sectional view of the tendons in a flat slab as all information relating to chairs can be shown on plan (see Fig. H11). Information about the layout of chairs can be shown on a separate drawing. During construction, cable chairs are placed in a first operation and tendons during a second operation.

Design
ormation

H2.1. Flat slab construction
(See Fig. H2.)

Total length in x-direction: 89·60 m.

Total length in y-direction: 37·10 m.

Spans in x-direction: 2·30 m, 5·00 m, $10 \times 7\cdot50$ m, 5·00 m, 2·30 m

Spans in y-direction: 0·775 m, 5·775 m, $3 \times 8\cdot00$ m, 5·775 m, 0·775 m

Slab thickness: $d = 250$ mm.

Column dimensions

rows A and F	250 mm × 250 mm
rows B and E	350 mm × 350 mm
rows C and D	300 mm × 300 mm

One opening at each column, 120 mm dia. (see Fig. H5).

H2.2. Loading conditions
(See Fig. H3.)

Dead load

$g_0 = 6\cdot25$ kN/m^2 (slab thickness)

$g_1 = 1\cdot75$ or 2·00 kN/m^2 (cover)

$G = 10\cdot0$ kN/m (façade load) (rows A, C, D and F)

Live load

$q = 3\cdot0$ kN/m^2 (offices)

H2.3. Materials

Concrete   *2.1.1*
C35

Compressive strength: $f_{ck} = 35$ N/mm^2 *2.1.2*

Shear stress: $\tau_{Rd} = 0\cdot38$ N/mm^2 *Table 4.3*

E-modulus: $E_{cm} = 33\cdot0$ kN/mm^2 *Fig. 2.4*

Shrinkage and creep   *2.1.7*

Equivalent thickness: $2A_c/u = d = 250$ mm

Atmospheric conditions: dry (relative humidity $\approx 55\%$)

t_0: fresh (3–7 days)

Shrinkage: $\varepsilon_{cs}(t_\infty, t_0) = 0\cdot35 \times 10^{-3}$ *Table 2.1*

Creep: $\phi(t_\infty, t_0) = 3\cdot5$

Prestressing time: 3 days

$\phi_1/\phi_\infty = 0\cdot10$ *Fig. 2.5*

Reinforcing steel   *2.2*
S400

Characteristic strength: $f_{yk} = 400$ N/mm^2 *2.2.1*

E-modulus: $E_s = 200$ kN/mm^2 *2.2.5*

Prestressing steel (BBRV Cona system)   *2.3*
Strands 0·6 in, S1570/1770

$A_p = 147$ mm^2

Characteristic strength: $f_{0\cdot1k} = 1570$ N/mm^2

Characteristic tensile strength: $f_{tk} = 1770$ N/mm^2

E-modulus: $E_s = 200$ kN/mm^2 *2.3.5*

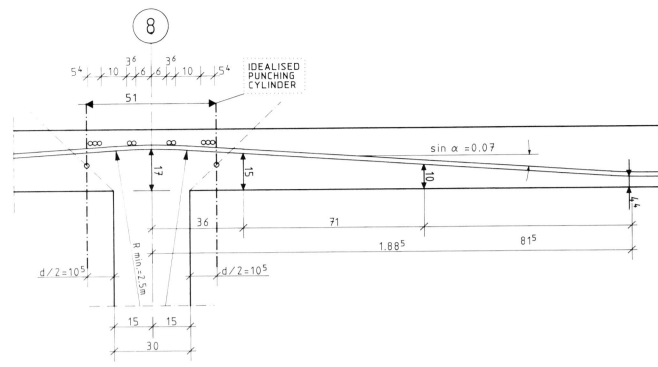

Fig. H4. Cable profile at support

Relaxation

    Initial steel stress: $\sigma_{p0}/f_{tk} = 0.7$

    Relaxation, steel group 2 (final value): 5.0%

                                                  Fig.

H2.4. Concrete cover

Normal exposure, cover	25 mm
Corrections for slabs	−5 mm

Chosen

Bottom	20 mm
Top	20 mm

Table

H2.5. Serviceability conditions

Deflection limit: $l/300$ (short term live load effect).

    $8000/300 = 27$ mm

Span/depth ratio: $8000/250 = 32$.

Crack limit: —

5.4.1

H3. Prestressing

H3.1. Tendons

Unbonded tendons (greased strands in polyethylene duct) with a diameter $\phi = 18$ mm were used. The tendons were located only within the support strip, and mainly concentrated within the idealized punching cylinder (see Figs H4 and H5).

    In the trapezoidal cable profile, the cable level d_p will change from a maximum at the support to its lowest value at quarter span (see Fig. H4).

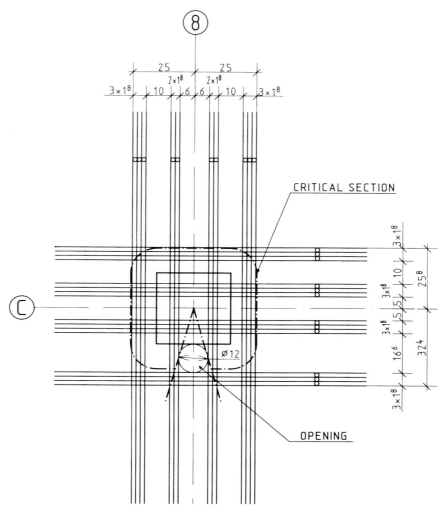

Fig. H5. Tendon distribution at support and periphery for punching shear

Cable in x-direction (secondary direction, first operation)

Quarter span: $l/4 = 7{\cdot}50/4 = 1{\cdot}875$ m.

d_p at support: 170 mm.

d_p at quarter span: 44 mm.

Inclination at critical section: $\sin \alpha_p = 0{\cdot}07$.

Cable in y-direction (main direction, second operation)

Quarter span: $l/4 = 8{\cdot}00/4 = 2{\cdot}00$ m.

d_p at support: 190 mm.

d_p at quarter span: 34 mm.

Inclination at critical section: $\sin \alpha_p = 0{\cdot}081$.

H3.2. Initial prestress

At the moment of tensioning   3.2

$$\sigma_{pi} = 0{\cdot}75 f_{tk} = 0{\cdot}75 \times 1770 = 1328{\cdot}0 \text{ N/mm}^2 \qquad 3.2.1$$

$$\begin{cases} < 0{\cdot}80 f_{tk} = 1416 \text{ N/mm}^2 \\ < 0{\cdot}90 f_{0.1k} = 1413 \text{ N/mm}^2 \end{cases}$$

Tendon force: $P_i = 147 \times 1328 = 195$ kN.

After transfer of prestress

$$\sigma_{p0} = 0.70f_{tk} = 0.70 \times 1770 = 1239.0 \text{ N/mm}^2$$

$$\begin{cases} <0.75f_{tk} = 1328 \text{ N/mm}^2 \\ <0.85f_{0.1k} = 1335 \text{ N/mm}^2 \end{cases}$$

Tendon force $P_0 = 147 \times 1239 = 182$ kN.

H3.3. Time of prestressing

3.2.2

The minimum compression cube strength at the anchorage zone was required to be $f_{cw3} = 20$ N/mm². The concrete and its admixtures were such that the value was reached within three days.

H3.4. Immediate losses

H3.4.1. Losses due to friction

3.3.2

Coefficient of friction: $\mu = 0.05$.
$k = 0.01$ m^{-1}

Losses for cables in x-direction

The tendon from anchor to anchor passes over four columns, with

sum of angular displacements $\alpha = 4 \times (4 \times 0.07) = 1.12$ rad

a total length of about $x = 4 \times 7.50 = 30.0$ m.

Maximum loss

$$\Delta\sigma_{pi} = \sigma_{pi}\{1 - \exp[0.05(1.12 + 0.01 \times 30)]\}$$

$$\Delta\sigma_{pi} = \sigma_{pi} \times 0.069$$

Losses for cables in y-direction

The tendon from anchor to anchor passes over four columns, with

sum of angular displacements $\alpha = 4 \times (4 \times 0.081) = 1.30$ rad

a total length of about $x = 3 \times 8.00 + 2 \times 6.55 = 37.10$ m.

Maximum loss

$$\Delta\sigma_{pi} = \sigma_{pi}\{1 - \exp[0.05(1.30 + 0.01 \times 37.1)]\}$$

$$\Delta\sigma_{pi} = \sigma_{pi} \times 0.08$$

Forces

The maximum losses at the far end of the tendon can almost be compensated by an initial tensioning to $P_i = 195$ kN.

$$P_0 = (1 - 0.069) \times 195 = 182.0 \text{ kN}$$

$$P_0 = (1 - 0.080) \times 195 = 180.0 \text{ kN} \approx 182.0 \text{ kN}$$

H3.4.2. Time-dependent losses

3.3.3

The main influences on time-dependent losses will be shrinkage and relaxation.

The vertical components of the prestressing forces are nearly in equilibrium with the dead load. Consequently, only small deflections and hardly any positive or negative moments are present. For losses due to creep, an overall mean value of 1.0 N/mm² compression stress can be assumed.

Losses due to creep

$$\Delta\sigma_p = \alpha\phi(t, t_0)\sigma_c$$

$$\alpha = E_s/E_c = 200/33 = 6.06$$

$$\Delta\sigma_p = 6.06(1 - 0.1) \times 3.5 \times 1.0 = 19.0 \text{ N/mm}^2$$

Losses due to shrinkage

$$\Delta\sigma_p = \varepsilon_s(t, t_0)E_s$$
$$= 0.35 \times 10^{-3}(1 - 0.1) \times 200 \times 10^3 = 63.0 \text{ N/mm}^2$$

Losses due to relaxation

$$\Delta\sigma_{pr} = 0.05 \times 1239.0 = 62.0 \text{ N/mm}^2$$

Correction factor

$$1 - \alpha(\sigma_{cpo}/\sigma_{po})(1 + \phi(t, t_0)/2)$$
$$= 1 - 6.06(-1.0/1239.0)(1 + 0.9 \times 3.5/2)$$
$$= 1.013$$

Total losses

$$\Delta\sigma_p = (19.0 + 63.0 + 62.0)/1.013 = 142.0 \text{ N/mm}^2$$
$$\Delta\sigma_p/\sigma_p = 142.0/1239 = 0.115 \quad (=11.5\%)$$

H3.5. Design calculation

3.4

As mentioned in the introduction, flat slabs are an ideal case for partial prestressing. The designer has the freedom to combine prestressing with reinforcing steel in order to fulfil the requirements of the ultimate limit state (ULS) (bending, punching shear) and those of the serviceability limit state (SLS) (cracking, deformation). To use only tendons within the support strips will be an extreme application for partial prestressing. For ULS, the high resistance is only put where it is really needed (bending moments within the support strips, punching shear). For SLS also, the vertical components of the tendons within the support strip will eliminate the main part of the deflections. All other requirements (bending resistance, cracking) will be met by the addition of reinforcing steel.

Thus the amount of prestressing will be chosen mainly according to tolerable deflection and cracking. ULS check provides the necessary reinforcing steel. The 'load-balancing method' is applied for the design of prestress for flat slabs. In general, the vertical components of the tendons will compensate at least the dead load and even some fraction of the live load.

3.4.3(e)

Design of the slab (ULS)

H4.1. Design principle

4.1

The static method of the theory of plasticity is chosen to determine the internal forces. Initial values for the moments are provided by an elastic calculation (in general, an approximate method such as the beam method will be used for flat slabs with regular spans). Thereafter, the negative support moments especially can be redistributed. In addition, the total moments at the supports and in the spans have to be distributed according to a dominant column strip and a less dominant middle strip. The sum of the resistances within the different strips has to be greater than the total acting moment.

Load factors

4.1.2

permanent loads $\gamma_g = 1.35$

Table 4.1

live loads $\gamma_q = 1.50$

As there is only one variable live load, the equation for the action forces is

$$(M, V)_{act\,d} = 1.35G + 1.50Q_1$$

Resistance factors

concrete $\gamma_c = 1.50$

steel $\gamma_s = 1.15$

4.1.3

Resistant action forces

$$(M, V)_{res\,d} = (M, V)(f_{ck}/1.50; f_{yk}/1.15; f_{0.1k}/1.15)$$

$$(M, V)_{act\,d} \leqslant (M, V)_{res\,d}$$

1.2

H4.2. Bending moments

The distribution of the total beam moment to the column and middle strips can be realized by factors, for which different proposals exist. It was decided to use here a small column strip (1/6 of the span). In addition, most of the total moment was taken to be within this region (70% at support, 50% in span). This kind of distribution is justified by the following arguments.

(a) Within the column strip there is a high bending moment resistance due to the prestressing steel.

(b) Prestressed structural elements (or even only a part of them) will attract action forces due to initial deformations (a so-called redistribution due to secondary moments).

The chosen distribution factors are shown in Table H1.

Table H1. Distribution factors

	Column strip	Middle strip	Column strip
Width of strip	0·167	0·666	0·167
Support moments	2·10 (35%)	0·45 (30%)	2·10 (35%)
Span moments	1·50 (25%)	0·75 (50%)	1·50 (25%)

Table H2. Moments in y-direction at supports, row 8

	Support A	Support B	Support C
Beam moment: kN m/m	− 15·0	− 70·0	− 85·0
Total moment: kN m	7·5 × 15·0 = 113·0	7·5 × 70·0 = 525·0	7·5 × 85·0 = 638·0
Column strip moment: kN m/m	2·1 × 15·0 = 32·0	2·1 × 70·0 = 147·0	2·1 × 85·0 = 179·0
Middle strip moment: kN m/m	0·45 × 15·0 = 7·0	0·45 × 70·0 = 32·0	0·45 × 85·0 = 38·0

Table H3. Moments in y-direction in spans, row 8

	Span A/B	Span B/C	Span C/D
Beam moment: kN m/m	24·1	44·9	40·1
Total moment: kN m	7·5 × 24·1 = 181·0	7·5 × 44·9 = 337·0	7·5 × 40·1 = 301·0
Column strip moment: kN m/m	1·5 × 24·1 = 36·0	1·5 × 44·9 = 68·0	1·5 × 40·1 = 60·0
Middle strip moment: kN m/m	0·75 × 24·1 = 18·0	0·75 × 44·9 = 34·0	0·75 × 40·1 = 30·0

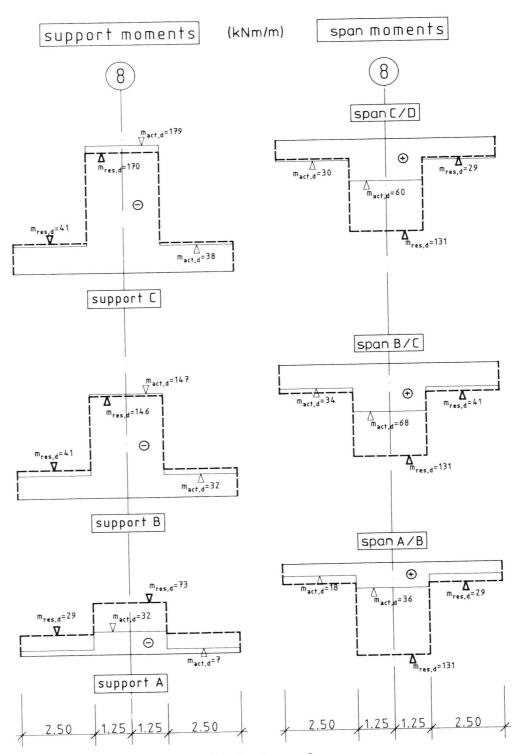

Fig. H6. Bending moments in y-direction for row 8

The moment results from the beam calculation and the corresponding distribution are shown below.

Acting moments, $m_{act,d}$
Moments in the y-direction are shown in Fig. H6 and Tables H2 and H3.

Moments in the x-direction are shown in Fig. H7 and Tables H4 and H5.

Resisting moments, $m_{res\,d}$

The resisting moments within the column strips will arise from a combination of prestressing and reinforcing steel, whereas in the middle strips only reinforcing steel will contribute. The calculation is based on the following tendon layout and its resulting values.

In the x-direction

	Strip A	Strip B	Strip C
Number of tendons	5	6	12
Area of steel	735 mm^2	882 mm^2	1764 mm^2

Level d_p of tendons at support: 179 mm

Level d_p of tendons in span: 209 mm

Maximum tendon length, L: $(15 + 30)/2 = 22\cdot50$ m

In the y-direction for strip 8

Number of tendons: 10

Area of steel: 1470 mm^2

Level d_p of tendons at support: 199 mm

Level d_p of tendons in span: 197 mm

Maximum tendon length, L: $37\cdot10$ m

The maximum stress for unbonded tendons even at ULS is identical with the stress after the transfer of prestress diminished by all losses

$$\sigma_{p\infty} = 0\cdot70 f_{tk} - \Delta\sigma_p = 1239\cdot0 - 142\cdot0 = 1097\cdot0 \text{ N/mm}^2$$

But account can be taken of a small increase in the stress at ULS due to a maximum span deflection of $f = l/50$. The resultant tendon elongation within a span is   *4.1.1*

$$\Delta l = 3fd/l = d/17$$

Table H4. Moments in x-direction at supports, row 8

	Support A	Support B	Support C
Beam moment: kN m/m	$-76\cdot0$	$-77\cdot0$	$-82\cdot0$
Total moment: kN m	$3\cdot67 \times 76\cdot0 = 278\cdot0$	$6\cdot9 \times 77\cdot0 = 530\cdot0$	$8\cdot0 \times 82\cdot0 = 656\cdot0$
Column strip moment: kN m/m	$2\cdot1 \times 76\cdot0 = 160\cdot0$	$2\cdot1 \times 77\cdot0 = 162\cdot0$	$2\cdot1 \times 82\cdot0 = 172\cdot0$
Middle strip moment: kN m/m	$0\cdot45 \times 76\cdot0 = 34\cdot0$	$0\cdot45 \times 77\cdot0 = 35\cdot0$	$0\cdot45 \times 82\cdot0 = 37\cdot0$

Table H5. Moments in x-direction in span 7/8

	Row A	Row B	Row C
Beam moment: kN m/m	$38\cdot0$	$38\cdot4$	$41\cdot0$
Total moment: kN m	$3\cdot67 \times 38\cdot0 = 139\cdot0$	$6\cdot9 \times 38\cdot4 = 265\cdot0$	$8\cdot0 \times 41\cdot0 = 327\cdot0$
Column strip moment: kN m/m	$1\cdot5 \times 38\cdot0 = 57\cdot0$	$1\cdot5 \times 38\cdot4 = 58\cdot0$	$1\cdot5 \times 41\cdot0 = 62\cdot0$
Middle strip moment: kN m/m	$0\cdot75 \times 38\cdot0 = 29\cdot0$	$0\cdot75 \times 38\cdot4 = 29\cdot0$	$0\cdot75 \times 41\cdot0 = 31\cdot0$

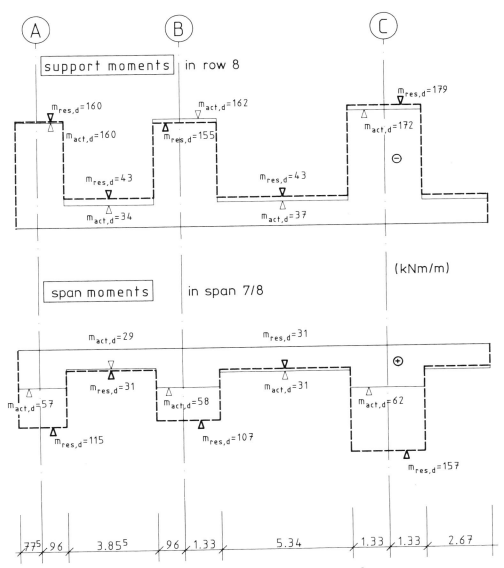

Fig. H7. Bending moments in x-direction for rows A, B and C

(see recommendations for the design of flat slabs,[1] R3.4.1.12) and the resultant stress increase is

$$\Delta\sigma_u = (\Delta l/L)E$$

where L is tendon length and E is E-modulus of steel). For support sections

$$\Delta\sigma_u = (\Delta l_1 + \Delta l_2)/LE$$

Stress increase x-direction

    span: $\Delta\sigma_u = [(0{\cdot}209/17)/22{\cdot}5] \times 200 \times 10^3 = 109 \text{ N/mm}^2$

    support: $\Delta\sigma_u = [2(0{\cdot}179/17)/22{\cdot}5] \times 200 \times 10^3 = 187 \text{ N/mm}^2$

Stress increase y-direction

    span: $\Delta\sigma_u = [(0{\cdot}197/17)/37{\cdot}1] \times 200 \times 10^3 = 62 \text{ N/mm}^2$

    support: $\Delta\sigma_u = [2(0{\cdot}199/17)/37{\cdot}1] \times 200 \times 10^3 = 126 \text{ N/mm}^2$

For the following calculation, a reduced concrete stress is used according to the simplified stress block.

$$\sigma_c = 0{\cdot}80 f_{ck}/\gamma_c = 0{\cdot}80 \times 35/1{\cdot}5 = 18{\cdot}6 \text{ N/mm}^2$$

Fig. 4.4

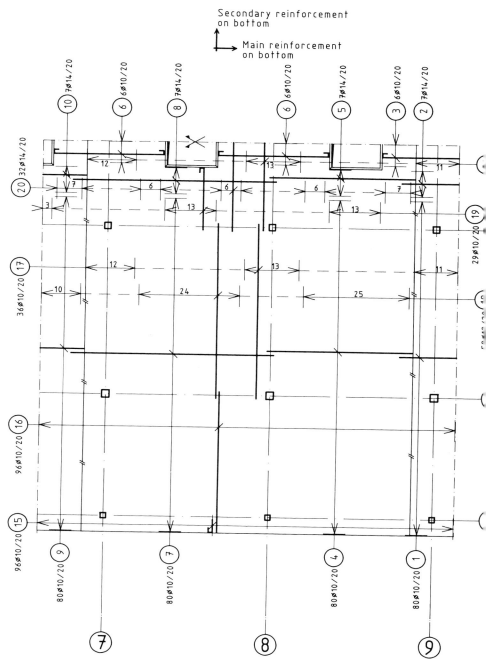

Fig. H8. Layout of bottom reinforcement

For reinforcing steel

$$f_{yd} = f_{yk}/\gamma_c = 400/1.15 = 348 \text{ N/mm}^2$$

The calculation in detail is shown only for column strip C in the x-direction (see Fig. H7).

Strip width 2·66 m, area of tendons, A_p, 1764 mm², depth of tendon, d_p, 179 mm.

Tendon stress

$$\sigma_u = (1097 + 187)/1.15 = 1117 \text{ N/mm}^2$$

Tendon force

$$F_p = 1764.0 \times 1117.0/1000 = 1970 \text{ kN}$$

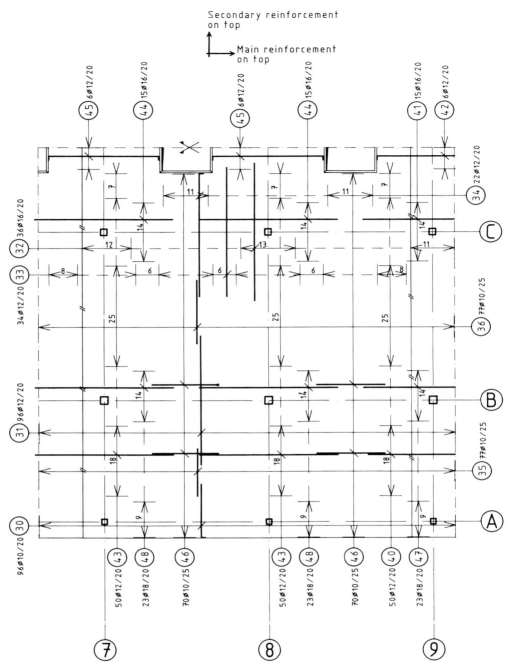

Fig. H9. Layout of top reinforcement

Area of reinforcement

$$A_\mathrm{s} = 1010 \times 2\cdot66 = 2686 \text{ mm}^2$$

(bars 16 mm dia. at 200 mm spacing).

Depth of steel, d_s, 220 mm.

Steel force

$$F_\mathrm{s} = 2686 \times 348 = 935 \text{ kN}$$

Concrete force

$$F_\mathrm{c} = 1970 + 935 = 2905 \text{ kN}$$

Compression zone

$$0 \cdot 8x = 2905/(2 \cdot 66 \times 18 \cdot 6) = 58 \text{ mm}$$

Moment

$$M_{\text{res d}} = 1970(0 \cdot 179 - 0 \cdot 029) + 935(0 \cdot 220 - 0 \cdot 029) = 476 \cdot 0 \text{ kN m}$$

$$m_{\text{res d}} > m_{\text{act d}}$$

$$476/2 \cdot 66 = 179 \cdot 0 > 172 \cdot 0$$

Note. Although the tendon force is concentrated within a very small zone, the total strip width was used for the compression zone. It can be imagined that the cross-section will behave like an idealized T-beam. To guarantee this behaviour, reinforcement is needed perpendicular to the direction of the tendons. In any case, there will be enough reinforcement in either of the two directions.

For a middle strip, reinforcing steel is as follows.

Area of reinforcement, A_s, 565 mm^2/m (bars 12 mm dia. at 200 mm spacing).

Depth of steel, d_s, 220 mm.

Steel force

$$F_s = 565 \times 348 = 197 \text{ kN/m}$$

Concrete force, F_c, 197 kN/m.

Compression zone

$$0 \cdot 8x = 197/(1 \cdot 00 \times 18 \cdot 6) = 10 \cdot 6 \text{ mm}$$

Moment

$$m_{\text{res d}} = 197(0 \cdot 220 - 0 \cdot 0053) = 43 \cdot 0 \text{ kN m/m}$$

$$m_{\text{res d}} > m_{\text{act d}}$$

$$43 \cdot 0 > 37 \cdot 0$$

All other resisting moments are calculated in the same way. Figs H6 and H7 show the results in comparison with the action moments. The reinforcing steel is shown in Figs H8 and H9.

Note. It can be seen that at different zones the resisting moment will be slightly less than the action moment. Such tiny modification can be allowed. It can be seen also that the resisting span moment within the column strip is much greater than the action moment. This should allow the moments to be redistributed from the support to the span. This was prevented by two arguments.

(a) Beside the prestressing steel, a minimum amount of reinforcing steel is required on top of the support zones, at least $\rho_s = 0 \cdot 3\%$; the resulting resisting moment will in general be enough to cover the support moment without any redistribution.
(b) There is no limit for a minimum resisting support moment (the new Swiss code demands a minimum moment depending on the punching shear resistance).

Table H6. *Forces at supports, row 8 (kN)*

	Support A	Support B	Suppor
Dead load, G_1	174·0	453·0	494·
Façade load, G_2	83·7	−14·3	77·
Total permanent load, $\sum G = G_1 + G_2$	257·7	438·7	571·
Live load, Q_1	65·3	170·3	182·
Design force, $V_{\text{Sd}} = 1 \cdot 35G + 1 \cdot 50Q$	446·0	848·0	1045·

H4.3. Ductility 4.2.4
The calculation in detail is shown only for column strip C at support.

$$\rho_s = 1010/(1000 \times 250) = 0.004$$

$$\rho_p = 1764/(2660 \times 250) = 0.003$$

$$\rho_{id} = 0.004 + 0.003 \times 1170/400 = 0.012 < 0.02$$

Ductility is sufficient.

All other values at supports will also satisfy the requirement.

H4.4. Punching shear 4.4.4
Forces at supports are shown in Table H6.

Acting shear

$$v_{Sd} = V_{Sd}/u$$

Resisting shear

$$v_{Rd} = v_{Rd1} + (1/u) \sum A_p \sigma_{p0} \sin \alpha_p$$ 4.4.4(b)

$$v_{Rd1} = 1.6 \tau_{Rd} d(1 + 50\rho_1)\kappa$$

(see recommendations for the design of flat slabs,[1] R3.4.1.241).

To calculate the resisting shear, the original formula from MC78 was used, with the extension $\kappa = 1.6 - d$ (d in metres). In addition, the extension due to the prestressing compression force was set at $1 + M_0/M_S = 1$, as in fact the small prestressing force will hardly influence the decompression moment M_0.

The following values are used.

Shear stress: $\tau_{Rd} = 0.38$ N/mm².

Depth of reinforcement

$$d = \tfrac{1}{2}(d_x + d_y) = 210 \text{ mm}$$

Correction factor

$$\kappa = 1.6 - d = 1.6 - 0.21 = 1.39$$

Critical section: u.

Longitudinal reinforcement

$$\rho_1 = \sqrt{(\rho_{1x}\rho_{1y})} \leqslant 0.008$$

(prestressing influence will be included with ρ_{px} and ρ_{py}).

Vertical components of the prestressing force within the critical section

$$A_p \sigma_0 \sin \alpha_p$$

Critical sections
The opening (dia. 120 mm) close to the columns reduces the critical section by Δu (see Fig. H5).

Column A (close to free edge)

$$u = 3 \times 250.0 + d\pi3/4$$

$$= 750.0 + 495.0 = 1245.0 \text{ mm}$$

(opening towards free edge).

Column B

$$u = 4 \times 350.0 + d\pi - \Delta u$$

$$= 1400.0 + 660.0 - 143.0 = 1917.0 \text{ mm}$$

Column C

$$u = 4 \times 300 \cdot 0 + d\pi - \Delta u$$

$$= 1200 \cdot 0 + 660 \cdot 0 - 146 \cdot 0 = 1714 \cdot 0 \text{ mm}$$

Longitudinal reinforcement

The influence of prestressing can be taken into account

$$\rho_{px, y} = P_{\infty x, y}/(l_{x, y} \, df_{sy})$$

(see recommendations for the design of flat slabs,[1] R3.4.1.241)

$$\rho_{px} = 46 \times 182 \cdot 0/(37 \cdot 10 \times 250 \cdot 0 \times 400) = 0 \cdot 0023$$

$$\rho_{py} = 10 \times 182 \cdot 0/(7 \cdot 50 \times 250 \cdot 0 \times 400) = 0 \cdot 0024$$

The total longitudinal reinforcement is shown in Table H7.

Vertical forces due to prestressing

x-direction: $P_0 \sin \alpha_p$

support A, B, C: $2 \times 182 \cdot 0 \times 0 \cdot 07 = 25 \cdot 5$ kN

y-direction: $P_0 \sin \alpha_p$

support A: $1 \times 182 \cdot 0 \times 0 \cdot 064 = 11 \cdot 7$ kN

support B, C: $2 \times 182 \cdot 0 \times 0 \cdot 081 = 29 \cdot 5$ kN

See Table H8.

Shear forces

Column A

$$v_{Sd} = 446 \cdot 0/1 \cdot 245 = 358 \cdot 0 \text{ kN/m}$$

$$v_{Rd1} = 1 \cdot 6 \times 0 \cdot 38 \times 210 \cdot 0 \times (1 + 50 \times 0 \cdot 0058) \times 1 \cdot 39$$

$$= 229 \cdot 0 \text{ kN/m}$$

Table H7. Longitudinal reinforcement, row 8

	Support A	Support B	Support C
Reinforcement in x-direction			
diameter: mm	18	18	16
spacing: mm	200	200	200
ρ_{sx}: %	0·58	0·58	0·45
ρ_{px}: %	0·23	0·23	0·23
Reinforcement in y-direction			
diameter: mm	10	12	16
spacing: mm	200	200	200
ρ_{sy}: %	0·18	0·27	0·49
ρ_{py}: %	0·24	0·24	0·24
ρ_l: %	0·58	0·64	0·71

Table H8. Vertical forces due to prestressing, row 8 (kN)

	Support A	Support B	Support C
$\sum P_0 \sin \alpha_x$	127·0	153·0	229·0*
$\sum P_0 \sin \alpha_y$	117·0	295·0	295·0
$\sum P_0 \sin \alpha$	244·0	448·0	524·0

* Only nine out of twelve tendons are taken into account for shear resistance, as three tendons lie outside the critical section (see Fig. H5).

$$358{\cdot}0 < 229{\cdot}0 + 244{\cdot}0/1{\cdot}245 = 425{\cdot}0$$

Column B

$$v_{Sd} = 848{\cdot}0/1{\cdot}917 = 442{\cdot}0 \text{ kN/m}$$

$$v_{Rd1} = 1{\cdot}6 \times 0{\cdot}38 \times 210{\cdot}0 \times (1 + 50 \times 0{\cdot}0064) \times 1{\cdot}39$$

$$= 234{\cdot}0 \text{ kN/m}$$

$$442{\cdot}0 < 234{\cdot}0 + 448{\cdot}0/1{\cdot}917 = 467{\cdot}0$$

Column C

$$v_{Sd} = 1045{\cdot}0/1{\cdot}714 = 610{\cdot}0 \text{ kN/m}$$

$$v_{Rd1} = 1{\cdot}6 \times 0{\cdot}38 \times 210{\cdot}0 \times (1 + 50 \times 0{\cdot}0071) \times 1{\cdot}39$$

$$= 240{\cdot}0 \text{ kN/m}$$

$$610{\cdot}0 > 240{\cdot}0 + 524{\cdot}0/1{\cdot}714 = 546{\cdot}0$$

The shear resistance at column C is insufficient. Punching shear reinforcement is needed.

$$v_{Sd} \leqslant 1{\cdot}6 v_{Rd1} + (1/u) \sum A_p \sigma_{p0} \sin \alpha_p \qquad \textit{4.4.4(c)}$$
$$1{\cdot}6 \times 240 + 306{\cdot}0 = 690{\cdot}0 > 610{\cdot}0$$

Design of punching shear reinforcement

$$V_{wd} = V_{Sd} - \sum A_p \sigma_{p0} \sin \alpha_p$$
$$A_{sw} = V_{wd}/(f_{sk}/\gamma_s)$$
$$V_{wd} = 1045 - 524{\cdot}0 = 521{\cdot}0 \text{ kN}$$
$$A_{sw} = 521{\cdot}0/0{\cdot}348 = 1497{\cdot}0 \text{ mm}^2$$

Different layers of reinforcement are put around the face of the support. The first one starts at a distance of

$$0{\cdot}5d = 0{\cdot}5 \times 210 = 105 \text{ mm} \qquad \textit{7.2.2}$$

and the last one will be at a distance of

$$d/\tan 30^\circ = 210/0{\cdot}58 = 370 \text{ mm} \qquad \textit{Fig. 4.8}$$

The spacing in between will be

$$s \leqslant 0{\cdot}6d = 0{\cdot}6 \times 210 = 126 \text{ mm}$$

Gives chosen $s = 120$ mm.

Serviceability limit state

H5.1. Checks carried out

5

As mentioned earlier, the prestressing of flat slab structures will be designed by the load-balancing method. As a design criterion we could require no deformations for a defined fraction of the load. The vertical components of such a prestress will at least compensate the dead loads and even parts of the live loads. Deflections and action moments will in general be very low. The main parts of the slab remain in a homogeneous state except the support zones, which may be cracked. The requirements for serviceability limit state will in general be satisfied when the deformations are checked and the minimum reinforcement is provided. Therefore interest will focus on

(a) deformations

(b) crack control by minimum reinforcement.

All other requirements such as

plan view   sectional view

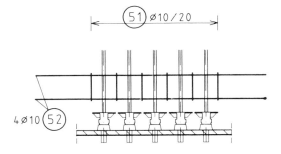
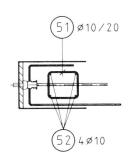

Fig. H10. Layout of spalling reinforcement

(*a*) stress limitation

(*b*) calculation of the crack width

will implicitly be fulfilled by the former checks.

H5.2. Deformations

5.4

In this example the dead loads will cause the main deformations. For calculation of the deformations, the live loads or a fraction of them can be neglected. The deflection limit was chosen as $l/300 = 8000/300 = 27$ mm.

An inner field of a flat slab will deform under dead load g

$$a_0 = 0.00581 g l^4/D$$

(see Friedrich[2])

$$D = E_{cm} d^3/[12(1 - v^2)]$$

If the column strip is supported with the vertical components of the prestressing forces (vertical forces equal dead load), the deformations will be

$$a_0 = 0.00126 g l^4/D$$

This will be a reduction of about 78%.

In this example the vertical prestressing forces are equal to the dead load (see section H4.4: compare support forces due to $\sum G$ and $\sum P_0 \sin \alpha_p$).

$$D = 3.3 \times 10^7 \times 0.25^3/[12(1 - 0.2^2)] = 4.5 \times 10^4 \text{ kN m}$$

$$a_0 = 0.00126 \times 8.25 \times 8^4/4.5 \times 10^4 = 1.0 \text{ mm}$$

If the slab is expected to be in a homogeneous state, the long term deflection will be

$$a_\infty = a_0(1 + \phi)$$

5.4.3

$$a_\infty = 1.0(1 + 3.5) = 4.5 \text{ mm}$$

And if some regions (support zones) of the slab are expected to be in   *Fig. 5.* a cracked state, the amplification factor will be about 6–8.

The maximum deflection that can be expected will be

$$a_\infty = 1.0 \times 8.0 = 8.0 \text{ mm}$$

($l/1000 = 8.0$ mm)

In comparison, for a flat slab without any prestressing, the value reached would be

$$a_\infty = (0.00581/0.00126) \times 8.0 = 4.6 \times 8.0 = 37.0 \text{ mm}$$

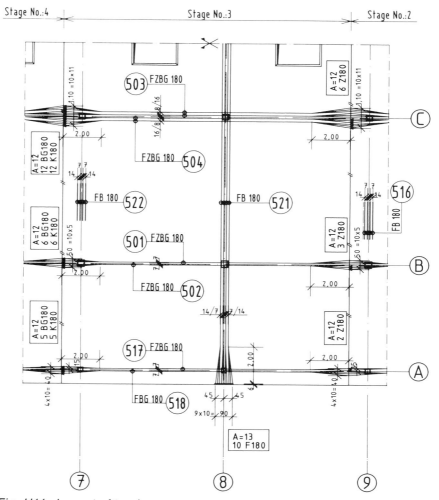

Fig. H11. Layout of tendons

The enormous advantage of prestressing flat slabs will be obvious from this result.

H5.3. Crack control
Minimum reinforcement

$$\rho_{r\,min} = A_s/A_{c\,ef}$$

$$h_{ef} = 250 \cdot 0/2 = 125 \cdot 0 \text{ mm}$$

$$A_{c\,ef} = 125 \times 1000 \cdot 0 = 125\,000 \cdot 0 \text{ mm}^2$$

bar spacing: $s = 200$ mm

$$\rho_{r\,min} = 0 \cdot 22\%$$

$$A_s = 0 \cdot 22 \times 1250 \cdot 0 = 275 \cdot 0 \text{ mm}^2$$

5.5
5.5.6

Fig. 5.5

The ULS checks provide more reinforcement than required, except in some zones of the top reinforcement between the column strips, where additional 10 mm dia. bars at 250 mm spacing were incorporated (area 314 mm²/m) (see Figs H8 and H9).

6. Detailing les

H6.1. Anchorage zones of tendons
Local force

$$F_{Sdu} = 1 \cdot 35 \times 1328 \cdot 0 \times 147 \cdot 0 = 264 \cdot 0 \text{ kN}$$

6.4

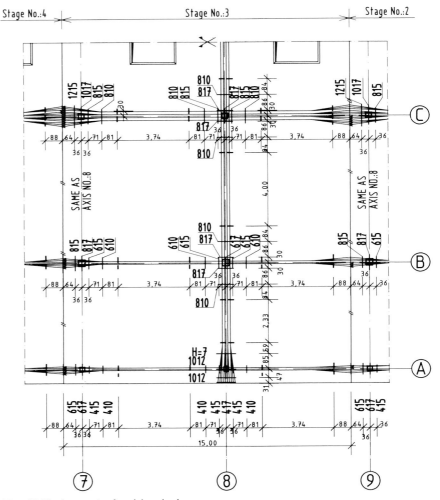

Fig. H12. Layout of cable chairs

Transverse tensile force

$$F_{Std} = 0.3 F_{Sdu}(1 - a_0/a_1)$$

$$a_1 = 250.0 \text{ mm}, a_0 = 136.0 \text{ mm}$$

$$F_{Std} = 0.3 \times 264.0 \times (1 - 0.55) = 36.0 \text{ kN}$$

Resisting force

reinforcement: two bars of 10 mm dia.; gives $A_s = 157.0 \text{ mm}^2$

$$F_{Rtd} = 157.0 \times 400.0/1.15 = 55.0 \text{ kN} > 36.0 \text{ kN}$$

See Fig. H10 for the arrangements of the reinforcement between the anchors.

H6.2. Detailing of reinforcement
The layout of the reinforcement for the four layers was carried out according to the ULS checks and the SLS requirements, and can be seen in Figs H8 and H9. Particular attention was given to the free edges of the slab (faces and openings), with special reinforcement perpendicular to the edges. This type of reinforcement can be seen in Fig. H8, position 15, 19, 6.

The layout of the tendons is shown in Fig. H11. The concept chosen for the anchors can be put into effect in the longitudinal direction. At each stage at least half of the tendons are stressed and fixed; the other half are stressed and fixed at the next stage. In the

6.5

middle of the building all tendons are fixed by anchors. Tendons crossing the strips in the other direction will all be stressed during each stage from the anchors at the façade side.

The layout of the cable chairs is shown in Fig. H12. The different chairs are symbolically marked and classified by a position number. The last two figures of the number indicate the height, and the first figures show the width.

The figure clearly demonstrates the idea of the trapezoidal tendon profile, as only a few cable chairs around a support are present. In addition, the pattern of the cable chairs will be nearly equivalent at each support point. This concept helps to standardize the tendon profile next to the support, and it can easily be checked during drawing and during execution on site.

eferences

1. *Recommendations for the design of flat slabs in post-tensioned concrete (using unbonded and bonded tendons)*. Fédération Internationale de la Précontrainte, London, 1980.
2. Friedrich T. *Entwurf und Bemessung von Decken in Spannbeton aufgrund von Gebrauchstauglichkeitskriterien*. BBR–VSL, Zurich–Berne, 1986.